MICHIGAN
GOLD
Mining in the Upper Peninsula

Lake Superior Port Cities Inc.

First Edition: September 1992

5   4   3   2   1

 LAKE SUPERIOR PORT CITIES INC.
P.O. Box 16417
Duluth, Minnesota 55816-0417
USA

PUBLISHER: James R. Marshall
DESIGN: Lynn Moore
EDITOR: Paul L. Hayden
ASSISTANT EDITOR: Tracy Claseman
TYPOGRAPHY: Stacy L. Winter
PRINTING: Cushing-Malloy Inc.

Library of Congress Cataloging-In-Publication Data

Fountain, Daniel R.
   Michigan Gold
   Bibliography, p. 156.
      1. Michigan 2. Upper Peninsula. 3. Lake Superior. 4. Mining. 5. Minerals.
6. Gold. 7. History. I. Title.

Library of Congress Card Catalog Number: 92-72995

ISBN 0-942235-15-0

Printed in the United States of America

This book is dedicated
to my wife, Judy,
for the years of encouragement,
suggestions, editing, love
and moral support.

Foreword

Ever since I was a child growing up in Ishpeming, Michigan, I had heard of the old Ropes Gold Mine, but never knew much about it. I shared a common misconception about gold mines, namely that they generally produced large nuggets of gold which anyone could find just by digging a bit. A couple of trips to the old mine's rock dumps and an ill-fated panning expedition to Gold Mine Creek (armed with a tin pie plate and plastic bags for my gold dust and nuggets) quickly dispelled these ideas, and I dismissed the Ropes as worthless.

When in the 1970s I began to hear that mining companies were surveying the area around the mine, I began to search out the history of the Ropes and Michigan gold mines, which, as far as I knew, were the only mines in the area. As I dug into the available resources, I learned to my surprise that gold prospects were spread throughout Marquette County and across the Upper Peninsula. This book is my attempt to compile the stories of these mines and miners.

As I started to search through the local libraries for information on the mines, I immediately found that no comprehensive recounting of the many gold prospects existed. Contemporary reports issued by the Michigan Geological Survey and the Commissioner of Mines and Mineral Statistics mentioned many of the major prospects; the files in the John M. Longyear Research Library at the Marquette County Historical Society told of others. Back issues of the *Engineering and Mining Journal* occasionally featured reports on the new mines and companies, and listed stock prices.

By far the richest source of information was the *Iron Ore,* Ishpeming's weekly newspaper from 1881 through 1953. George Newett, the paper's publisher, was a tireless backer of the city and especially its mining industries, both iron and gold. Nearly every new mining company was given a full write-up in his paper, including the location and extent of the exploration, the officers and financial arrangement of the company and, most importantly, how the reader could purchase stock in this promising young company! Newett was not one to pull his punches, however, being just as ready to condemn a mining company's management at the first sign of a swindle.

One disadvantage of relying on the press for historical information is the lack of any negative news about the prospects. As long as the gold veins held out, the promising company was news; but when the veins pinched or assays declined in value, the prospects were forgotten. By the same token, assay values published in the media must be read in context. Many prospects produced samples which held, by assay, several ounces of precious metal per ton of ore, yet were quickly abandoned. What was not reported was that not tons, but merely a few pounds or only ounces of the rich ore were available to be mined!

This book is intended as a history, rather than a prospector's guide. Although legal descriptions are given identifying the location of the land held by the early explorers, the prospects themselves are not pin-pointed. There are a couple of reasons for this. First, most of the prospects mentioned in this book lie on private property, and the owners do not always welcome visitors. Michigan trespass law requires the permission of the landowner before entering private land. Second is the matter of safety. Many of the shafts and adits dug a century ago are still open, lying hidden and forgotten in the woods. In some cases, water-filled shafts more than 100 feet deep are left unfenced, sur-rounded by mossy banks and piles of loose rock. Another reason I have not given the exact locations of some prospects is that they have (so far) eluded me!

Daniel Fountain
August 1992

Acknowledgments

The old time prospector is often portrayed as a loner with only his burro as a companion, but this modern literary "sourdough" could not have written this book without the contributions of many others. The author extends his sincere thanks to:

Jim Rouse, for sharing his knowledge of the Gogebic Range
Gene Londo, for showing me the Ropes
Fred Stonehouse, for his encouragement on both ends
Larry Roncaglione
Randy Leppala
Kay Wallace Porter
Fred Rydholm
Marquerite Grummett Bergdahl
Dick Nicholas and Ethel Valenzio
Jack Steve
Jack Deo of Superior View Studio
Linda Panian, Rachel Crary and Rosemary Michelin of the Marquette
    County Historical Society
Wattsson and Wattsson Jewelers of Marquette, who promote the use
    of Michigan Gold in their products
Willard Bodwell of Resource Exploration Incorporated
Fred Peterson of Longyear Realty Corporation
Ross Wayment and John Norby of Callahan Mining Corporation
Staff of the Carnagie Public Library, Ishpeming
Staff of the Peter White Public Library, Marquette
Staff of the Negaunee Historical Society
Staff of the Iron County Historical Society, Hurley, Wisconsin
Burton Boyum for his review of the manuscript
Kurt Fosburg and Nikki, my enthusiastic prospecting partners

Table of Contents

Michigan
Gold

PROSPECTING AREAS

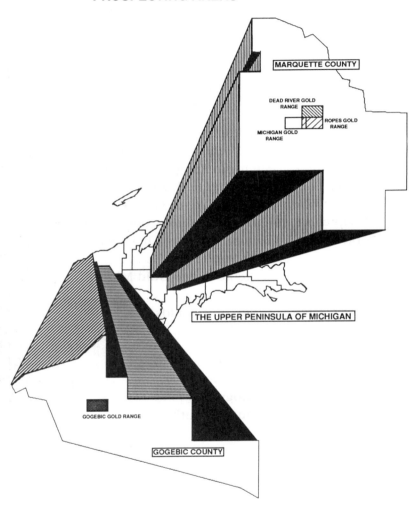

MARQUETTE COUNTY

DEAD RIVER GOLD
RANGE

ROPES GOLD
RANGE

MICHIGAN GOLD
RANGE

THE UPPER PENINSULA OF MICHIGAN

GOGEBIC GOLD RANGE

GOGEBIC COUNTY

Introduction

M ichigan's Upper Peninsula is an ancient, rugged land. The contorted surface of its western half stands in mute witness of its ancient fiery birth. This part of the peninsula is made up of the oldest rock in the world, the Canadian Shield, which is as much as four billion years old. Predating the earliest life on earth, this ancient formation is host to an array of valuable minerals. Copper, which is found in its native form in the U.P.'s Copper Country and on Isle Royale, was mined by prehistoric Native Americans thousands of years ago. Stories about massive pieces of the virgin metal which could be dug from the ground were related by early fur traders and missionaries on their return to civilization. A few mining ventures were begun. Once the rich copper deposits of the Keweenaw Peninsula were documented by Douglass Houghton, Michigan's first state geologist in 1841, a copper rush to the Lake Superior country began. Mining began in earnest in 1844 with the discovery of the Cliff Mine near Eagle River.

That same year, the rich iron deposits of the Marquette Iron Range were discovered near present-day Negaunee. A party of surveyors under William Austin Burt was running a range line when they noticed the compass making dramatic deviations from true north. A search of the surrounding area turned up specimens of high grade iron ore. Within a few years, the towns of Ishpeming and Negaunee were founded and the iron ore mining industry of the Upper Peninsula had begun.

Finding gold was one of the objectives of the earliest European explorers to visit the Lake Superior country, but the natives knew nothing of the yellow metal. The explorers soon turned their attention to the abundant copper and iron deposits. Small amounts

of gold were found as early as 1845, but it was not until the opening of the Ropes Gold Mine in the early 1880s that gold mining jumped into Michigan's history. The Ropes mine ran for 14 years and produced $645,792 in gold and silver, but was never able to pay a dividend to its stockholders.

In the years following the establishment of this first mine, more than 75 other gold mines and prospects were begun in the Upper Peninsula. Some, such as the Lake Superior and Michigan mines, produced spectacularly rich specimens of gold-bearing quartz. Other prospects consisted of only a few trenches and pits, producing no more than traces of the precious metal. Most prospecting had ceased by the early 1900s, but the Great Depression and the increase in the price of gold from $20.67 to $35 per ounce brought about another prospecting boom in the 1930s. World War II called a halt to gold mining, with the prospects lying idle until the abandonment of the gold standard in 1971 and the resultant dramatic rise

Douglass Houghton, discoverer of gold in Michigan
Michigan State Archives

in the price of gold. Improved metallurgical methods and higher gold prices in the 1970s and '80s attracted a $20 million redevelopment project to the Ropes mine, which again began producing gold in the fall of 1985. The reopened mine produced until 1989, when a combination of low gold prices, poor ore grade and a collapse of rock in the production shaft prompted its shutdown.

Gold was first discovered in Michigan by Douglass Houghton, the first state geologist. Appointed to the post by Governor Steven T. Mason in 1837, Houghton made several visits to the Upper Peninsula, reporting on the copper wealth existing there. In 1844, he convinced Congress to finance a joint geological and linear survey of Michigan. For the 1845 survey in the Upper Peninsula, Houghton worked with William Austin Burt, Deputy Land Surveyor for the federal government. While Burt and his crew located the range and township lines, marking their corners, Houghton's men took detailed geological notes and samples, and measured the land's elevation.

While camped near the present site of Negaunee in 1845, Houghton returned from a solo excursion with rock specimens carrying enough free gold to fill an eagle's quill. Fearing that his men would desert to prospect for gold, he kept the find a secret. Houghton only revealed the discovery to his trusted associate Samuel Worth Hill, the veteran mineral explorer whose penchant for spicy language has been immortalized in the euphemism "What the Sam Hill!" Unfortunately, Dr. Houghton drowned later that year when his canoe capsized in a storm near Eagle Harbor, and the exact location of his find died with him.

In June the following year, Houghton's younger brother, Jacob, found a vein of native copper on the Keweenaw Peninsula which held a small amount of gold. An assay by Robbins and Hubbard of Detroit yielded 10.25 ounces of copper, 1.75 ounces of silver and 12 grains of gold from a 28-ounce specimen. The assay produced a gold bead which Jacob Houghton wore for many years as the head of a stickpin.

Silas C. Smith, one of the first settlers in Marquette,

claimed a few months before his death that he had discovered mineral deposits containing gold and silver within the city limits in 1854 and 1855. Although Smith never developed his finds, later discoveries in the city support his claims.

The next evidence of gold in the area was discovered during the silver mining boom in 1864. During an assay of mineral specimens from the Silver Lake district 12 miles northwest of Ishpeming, assayers found economic quantities of gold in a sample of iron pyrite. Although more than 35 silver and gold mining companies were formed and thousands of acres of land were bought and sold during the boom, only a few mines were actually begun. Some of these shafts and adits produced small amounts of silver ore, but none became successful mines or reported any gold production. The last of these silver mines closed down in 1868.

In 1869, Waterman Palmer sold several parcels of land to the Cascade Iron Company near the town which bears his name. He revealed that a small vein of gold-bearing quartz existed there. The iron company sampled the vein and found up to $900 worth of gold per ton of ore (at $20.67 per troy ounce, the statutory price of gold until 1933). The vein was too small to be mined profitably and was soon forgotten.

CHAPTER ONE

The Ropes Gold Mine

I t was Julius Ropes who finally convinced the world that Michigan had gold in economic quantities. Born in 1835 in Newbury, Vermont, and educated at the St. Johnsbury Academy, Ropes came to Marquette County in 1855. Ropes worked in a store in Harvey, which was then known as Chocolay, delivering mail, hauling it by dog sled in the winter. He later joined Marquette's first mayor, Henry H. Stafford, in running a drug store in Marquette. In 1867 Ropes moved to Ishpeming and opened a pharmacy for Stafford. Their store was the second business in the young town, the first being a saloon. Ropes soon bought out Stafford's interest in the store, going into business on his own as J. Ropes & Company. In 1868 he married Silas Smith's niece, Eunice Louisa Rouse, served as Ishpeming's postmaster and was a member of the first school board. Ropes recognized the potential for precious metal mining in Marquette County and as early as 1874 advertised that he performed fire assays of gold and silver ores. In 1878 he sold his pharmacy business to F.P. Tillson, but continued his assay work from an office on Main Street, above his brother-in-law's shoe store.

In the late-1870s, woodcutters chopping wood for the charcoal kilns of the Deer Lake Furnace brought Ropes specimens of what they thought was petrified wood. Ropes identified the mineral as a type of asbestos. He explored the area where the "petrified wood" had been discovered and found a range of

Julius Ropes, discoverer of the Ropes Gold Mine
Superior View Studio

hills with outcroppings of a green serpentine marble which he recognized as having commercial value.

Ropes bought the mineral rights to the S ½ of the NW ¼ of Section 29, T48N-R27W, in 1879, and along with Dr. William T. Carpenter, Solomon S. Curry and George P. Cummings, a fellow Vermonter who was married to Ropes' sister, Hannah, founded the Huronian Marble Company. Aside from cutting and polishing a number of specimens, Ropes did little with the property, but continued to explore, realizing that the geology of the serpentine range was favorable for precious metals. He soon found a small vein of quartz that looked promising for silver. Upon testing the ore in his laboratory, he found that it contained both gold and silver.

On May 17, 1881, Ropes stuck his prospecting pick into a mossy rock outcrop and revealed a vein of quartz containing $21 per ton in gold, enough for commercial exploitation. Ropes sank an 11-foot shaft on this vein and found that the lode widened from a few inches at the surface to two feet at the bottom. Samples of gold-bearing quartz from the shaft were found to be worth up to $367 per ton.

In August, the Ropes Gold and Silver Company was formed, with Ropes, Cummings, Curry and Carpenter as partners. Capital stock was $1 million, consisting of 40,000 shares at $25 each. The company bought the eastern half of the Huronian Company's land for $5,000. During the winter of 1881-82, the company

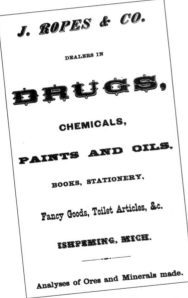

Early Ropes Advertisement
Beard's Directory & History of Marquette County, 1873

2

sank a second shaft known as the "B" shaft about a quarter mile west of the "A" shaft at the discovery point. Assays of specimens from this shaft ranged from $18 to $59 per ton in gold and silver. A series of trenches dug across the strike of the vein traced it several hundred feet farther west onto the Huronian Company's land.

At the March 12, 1883, stockholders' meeting, it was decided to purchase the rest of the Huronian Marble Company's land for $20,000 and to sink an 8-by-10-by-40 foot main shaft at the vein's richest spot. This shaft, named the Curry shaft after mine superintendent S.S. Curry, eventually became the only production shaft and eventually reached a depth of 813 feet. By midsummer, the new shaft had reached a depth of 30 feet. A steam-powered pump had been installed to keep the workings dry, and a barbed wire fence had been added to keep the curious at a distance. A large dog named Bouncer assisted in the guard duties.

In August 1883 a small Fraser and Chalmers stamp mill was installed, and the first batch of ore was processed. After a run of 39 days, the company recovered a total of 40 ounces of gold, worth $830, and 158 ounces of silver worth $173 from 100 tons of rock. Local newspapers heralded the production as "A

Ropes Stock Certificate
Negaunee Historical Society

3

Golden Bonanza!'' and the first "bullion train" (actually a horse-drawn wagon) in Michigan carried the gold from the mine to Ishpeming for public display. The Ropes mill made two more runs totalling 172 tons, yielding $820 in gold and $176 in silver, before shutting down for the winter. The bullion was shipped to the Philadelphia mint for refining. When the first coins minted from Michigan gold were received in December, they were eagerly sought as collectors' items.

Following this demonstration of the feasibility of gold mining, many more prospects were opened on the Ishpeming Gold Range, as the belt of serpentine hills west of the Ropes property became known. (For the purposes of this book, the author has divided the Ishpeming Gold Range into two parts: the Michigan Range, including the prospects near the Michigan Gold Mine on R28W, and the Ropes Range, which includes properties in R27W, near the Ropes Mine.) The most famous of these was the Michigan Gold Mine, 2½ miles southwest of the Ropes, which produced

some spectacular specimens of free gold — so spectacular, in fact, that "the trunk of one enterprising fellow who was all ready to take his departure for Europe was looked into and found to contain over two thousand dollars' worth of golden treasure, secured from this property when the eyes of the bosses were not upon him."

Underground development work and mining resumed in April 1884, and the mill reopened in June, financed by the sale of 24,000 shares of stock. Over the summer the small mill stamped some 163 tons of ore, yielding $2,613 in gold and silver. In the fall of 1884, the company decided to enlarge the mill from five to 25 stamps, and the expanded mill, housed in a new 56-by-76 foot, three-story building, went into production in November of the same year. The new mill

Solomon S. Curry
Biographical Record

4

building was connected to the shafthouse by a trestle. Tram cars were loaded at the shafthouse and pushed across the trestle to the top floor of the mill, where the ore was dumped onto a coarse screen called a grizzly. The grizzly separated the large chunks of ore, which were crushed in a Blake jaw crusher, from the fine ore which bypassed the crusher and was fed into the Fraser and Chalmers Cornish stamp mills.

Fig. 24.—Recent stamp mill. *(From Traylor Eng. & Mfg. Co.)*

The Cornish stamp mill, named for Cornwall, England, where it originated, consisted of five cast iron stamp heads or pestles which were alternately raised and dropped onto an iron die in a common mortar. Five such mills, or stamp batteries, were installed at the Ropes. The cylindrical stamp heads, each weighing 750 pounds, were raised eight inches by a camshaft turned by steam power, then allowed to drop 66 times per minute, crushing the coarse ore in the mortar, which was kept nearly full of mercury. In addition to crushing the ore, the stamps also brought the particles of free gold into close contact with the mercury, forming an amalgam — a soft alloy of gold, silver and mercury. Punched metal screens across the outlet of the mortar kept the ore and amalgam in the mill until it was finely ground. Tullock automatic feeders kept a constant level of coarse ore in the mill, and a continuous flow of water washed the fine ore and amalgam out through the screens and onto the amalgam-collecting plates. These plates, inclined 48-by-120-inch sheets of silver-plated copper, would catch the metallic amalgam while the waste rock was washed through a trough to the vanner room, 10 feet below and to the north of the stamp room.

After a run of two weeks to a month, depending on the richness of the ore, the flow of ore to the stamp

Cornish Stamp Mill
Daniel Fountain
collection

battery would be halted and the mill stopped for cleanup. All of the gold-mercury amalgam would be

removed from the mortar and plates and retorted (distilled), boiling off the mercury and condensing it for reuse, leaving the gold behind. The mortar was then refilled with mercury and another run was begun.

A great deal of the gold and silver in the Ropes ore could not be recovered by mercury amalgamation, because it was locked up in sulfide minerals, including pyrite, chalcopyrite and galena. These values were recovered from the stamp mill tailings by gravity separation within Frue vanners. The Frue vanner, developed by William

Bell Frue, the superintendent of the famous Silver Islet mine near the Sibley Peninsula in Ontario, was an endless rubber belt which traveled up a slight incline at six feet per minute while vibrating from side to side at 200 strokes per minute. The stamp mill tailings were fed in a water slurry onto the belt near the top of its slope. The heavy mineral-bearing pyrite settled on the belt and was carried over the upper end, while the lighter quartz rock was kept in suspension by the vibration and washed off the lower end. These tailings were dumped into the valley to the north of the mill, while the mineral-rich concentrate was sent for refining to a smelter in Aurora, Illinois.

Inside its wooden building, the mill was able to run even in sub-zero winter temperatures. By the end of 1884, the shaft was 85 feet deep and producing on two levels. Other improvements were made at the site that year, which included adding a boarding house for the

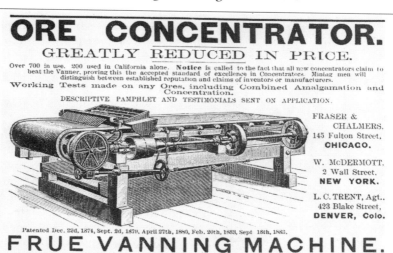

miners, carpenter and blacksmith shops, an assay office, a warehouse and a barn. The hoisting plant formerly used at the Dexter iron mine, good for a depth of 300 feet, was installed at the shaft. The stream in the valley just to the north was dammed with an earth dam and was reinforced with tailings to increase the

Stamp mills (background) and vanner engine in 1884 mill building
Marquette County Historical Society

Engineering and Mining Journal

new mill's water supply. Mining and milling continued on two shifts until October 1885, when the night shift was discontinued in an effort to conserve the scarce working capital. By that time, the shaft had reached 250 feet with four levels.

1886 saw the introduction of power drills at the mine, financed by a 10-cent-per-share assessment. Powered by air from a steam-driven compressor, the four Rand "Little Giant" drills allowed the force of miners to be cut from 30 to 12, and permitted drifting to be carried out at a rate of 3½ feet per day. During July, a prolonged drought dried up the mill's water supply, so another dam was built at the junction of three small streams about a mile to the west and a pipeline was run to the mill.

Nearly 50 men were now working in the mine and mill, enjoying the new steam-heated dry house complete with hot and cold running water. The mine was opened down to the sixth level, with an estimated 38,000 tons of ore available for stoping. As the shaft

passed the 300-foot mark, the hoisting plant became inadequate, and a new six-foot hoist drum capable of lifting 1,200 pounds of ore was purchased from Marquette's Iron Bay Manufacturing Company.

Although the mine was 349 feet deep and producing from five of its six levels, by 1887 the lack of capital had taken its toll. Worn out equipment was not being maintained and the mill building itself was falling into disrepair. When Frank Cummings, an experienced gold miner from Colorado, took over from George Weatherston as superintendent in May, he immediately started a program of repair and renovation. He began by replacing a cracked stamp mill mortar, which was leaking precious gold-mercury amalgam onto the floor.

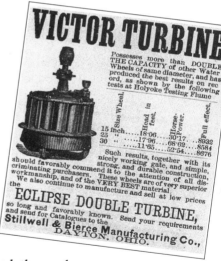

When the floor in the mill was replaced, the workers were actually able to scrape amalgam from the underlying timbers. Cummings was responsible for other improvements at the mine, including the installation of riffles in the tailrace to save gold from the tailings. He rerouted the oily steam engine exhaust, which had been interfering with the amalgamation process,

Curry shaft at left, Ely shaft and 1887 mill building at right
Marquette County Historical Society

Engineering and Mining Journal

away from the mill's water supply. He also introduced the six-day work week, feeling that "one day's rest each week harms no one." After three months, Cummings resigned, apparently in frustration over the lack of money needed to put the operation in proper order.

Further improvements were begun in 1887. It was decided to build a new mill building with room for 40 stamps, but initially equipped with 20. A six-foot-high wooden dam was built on the Carp River about three-quarters of a mile from the mine with a 20-inch Victor turbine driving a 5½-inch duplex Knowles pump to ensure a constant water supply to the mill. A new shaft, named the Ely for company secretary Clarence R. Ely, was started 350 feet east of the Curry shaft and sunk 75 feet during the year. To finance these improvements, another assessment of 50 cents was called in August.

The new mill began operation on May 17, 1888, adding 20 stamps to the existing 25, all running off a new 235-horsepower Corliss steam engine. With the new equipment nearly doubling the mill's capacity, the small, crooked shaft became a bottleneck, prompting the company to square up the shaft and to install a skip road (wooden rails on which the skip or ore bucket would ride). Down to the eighth level,

Curry shafthouse and 1887 mill building
Lake Superior Mining Institute

the shaft had followed the 80 degree southerly dip of the vein. It was decided that in order to increase hoisting efficiency, the shaft would be sunk vertically below that level, even though this would carry the shaft away from the gold-rich quartz vein.

Installing the skip road to the fifth level necessitated shutting down the mine and mill for more than a month in October and November, during which time a new shaft house was built and a new 30-ton-per-hour Gates gyratory crusher was installed, replacing the outmoded Blake jaw crusher. The Blake crusher had been located inside the old mill building, but the dust it produced caused excessive wear on the mill machinery. The new crusher, along with its own 50-horsepower engine, was installed in the shaft house.

A possible solution to the mining company's continuing capital shortage was proposed in 1888 by

General Russell A. Alger, who led a group of Detroit investors in an offer to buy a majority interest in the Ropes Gold and Silver Company. The stockholders rejected the offer, feeling that the three dollars per share offered was too low. Another 50-cent-per-share assessment was called in September.

By the end of the year, the Curry shaft was 441 feet deep with nine levels. A total of 62 men found employment at the mine in 1888: 40 miners and other underground workers, 15 men in the mill and seven *Engineering and Mining Journal*

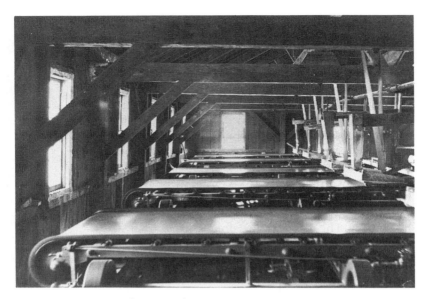

surface employees.

With reserves of high-grade ore still in sight, the company decided to complete their expansion in 1889 by installing another 20 heads of stamps, for a total of 65 heads in the two mill buildings, and four more vanners. The expanded mill went into operation on March 9. A larger air compressor capable of powering up to 12 drills was also added. The shaft was extended to the 11th level, a depth of 551 feet, and a Lane band friction hoist was installed, powered by the old stamp mill engine. The enlarged, improved mill, along with other cost-cutting measures, trimmed mining and milling overhead to $1.75 per ton. The gross production of $99,715.45 from 31,365 tons, the highest in the mine's history, left the company more than $6,000 in the black at the end of fiscal 1889.

During 1890, the Ropes company contracted with M.E. Harrington and Son of Ishpeming to search for additional quartz lenses with a diamond drill. This was the first underground diamond drill exploration on the Ishpeming Gold Range. The exploration program paid off almost immediately, with a vein of low grade ore being found north of the fifth level. This vein was mined by a crosscut from the Ely shaft.

Frue vanners in
1887 mill building
*Marquette County
Historical Society*

Another vein, assaying $60 per ton, was found 70 feet north of the 11th level later that summer. A drift was run toward this vein from the 10th level, but when it reached the vein, the quartz was only an inch wide. Fortunately, the lens widened out to five to six feet as it was traced to the 11th level. The mine was still in good shape at the end of 1890, the shaft being 639 feet deep with the skip road extending to the lowest level, the 12th. The previous year's profits had been spent, however, and another 25-cent-per-share assessment was called in February 1891.

The mine operated quietly during the next year, sinking the shaft to the 13th level. The old 25 stamp mill was shut down, leaving only the 40 heads running in the new mill building. The air compressor was enlarged to a duplex (two cylinder), doubling the number of power drills which could be used in the mine. Pay rock was mined from the fifth through the 13th levels.

Rich rock from an ore lens on the eighth and ninth levels, 200 feet from the shaft, allowed the mine to make a profit during the first two months of 1892, but by July a 25-cent-per-share assessment was called to ensure a supply of reserve capital to keep the mine open. A rich streak assaying up to $213 per ton was found the next month, but any profit from this was offset by the expense of drifting through worthless or low grade rock to get to the pay rock.

Lane's Patent Band Friction Hoists,

Improved Corliss and Slide Valve Engines, High Speed Straight Line Engines, Steam pumps, Boilers, Mining Cages, Skips, Cars, Ore Buckets, Sheaves and General Mining Machinery.

Contractors for Prospecting Coal or Mineral Lands.

—Standard Hoisting Drums 2 ft. to 25 ft. in Diameter.

Carbons for Drilling Purposes at Lowest Rates.

By December, when the night shift was cut out to reduce costs, rumors were being heard that the mine would close, but the reduced hours and the cessation of all development work, mining only the rock already exposed, allowed the mine's production to exceed expenses during the last months of the fiscal year. At the end of 1892, the shaft had reached 813 feet, 25 feet below the 15th

Engineering and Mining Journal

level, never to go deeper. Sinking vertically had carried the shaft away from the vein, necessitating costly drifting through poor rock. The financial crisis, which became known as the Panic of 1893, curtailed investors' ability to put needed capital into their businesses, so at the March 1893 annual meeting the superintendent recommended that further sinking be done in the rich ore body itself. Thus, all rock removed would be pay rock, theoretically cutting expenses.

The 15th level was extended more than 300 feet to the east into a large body of pay rock, where an incline was sunk 100 feet into the ore body. The quartz vein here was 12 feet thick and less mixed with slate than almost anywhere else in the mine. It carried an average of six dollars in gold but had specimens assaying up to $150. There was plenty of rock to supply the mill, but the added expense of hauling the ore up the incline and rehandling it at the 15th level ate up any profit, since extra workers and machinery were needed. The mine eventually reached its deepest depth of 915 feet below surface in an underhand stope at the bottom of the incline. Although the company explored on the surface for more veins, trenching across the strike of the vein west of the shafts and sinking a small exploratory shaft near the schoolhouse, most of the production over the next four years came from the bottom levels and from lenses previously exposed in the upper levels of the mine.

By 1897, the company's lack of working capital had finally caught up with it. A number of paydays had been missed over the last eight years until the back pay due the miners totaled about $3,000. On July 10, 1897, the 40 miners stopped work and filed suit to get their pay. On July 27, the suit was decided in the miners' favor. The property was turned over to a receiver, spelling the end of the Ropes Gold and Silver Company.

During its 14 years of operation, the mine had produced a total of $645,792 in gold and silver, with the best year's production being $99,715 in 1889. Although the company had operated in the black for

several years, what little profit that was made was put back into the mine. No dividends were ever paid to the stockholders. In fact, $2.34 per share in assessments was levied on the stock.

Part of the company's financial woes was caused

by the inefficiency of the mill and poor recovery of the gold. The Ropes mill processed the ore by stamping it in Cornish stamp mills. The stamp mills would work very well on hard, brittle rock such as quartz, but the Ropes ore contained a great deal of soft talcose slate, which tended to stick in the mortar, cushioning the blow.

The company continually sought to improve the

The Wiswell Ore Pulverizer and Electric Amalgamator

Engineering and Mining Journal

recovery of gold in the stamp mills. Early on, the original 60-mesh punched-metal screens which controlled the outlet from the mortars were replaced with 40-mesh wire screens, improving the flow of ground ore from the mill. Experiments were made on the frequency with which the stamp heads fell, starting with the original 66 blows per minute and finally settling on 88. A consistent flow of crushed ore to the mill was the intent behind the installation of Tullock automatic feeders in the 25 stamp mill in 1886. These shaking-table feeders tended to clog, however, and were replaced with Challenge disc feeders in the 40 stamp mill in 1888. Another improvement incorporated in the new mill was the use of 850-pound stamp heads in place of the 750-pound stamps in the original mill.

The company even considered replacing the stamp mills entirely, experimenting with the Wiswell Electric Ore Pulverizer, the Huntington centrifugal mill and the Crawford mill. The Wiswell Pulverizer, a variation of the Chilean mill, was tried in 1885. This machine consisted of an 8½-foot circular crushing box with a V-shaped groove. Four heavy iron wheels rotated by a central shaft rolled in this groove. Ore and mercury were fed into the groove, where the rotating

wheels crushed the ore. A large battery supplied electric current, which was passed through the pulp, supposedly assisting in amalgamation. At first the Wiswell machine seemed to be a success, recovering much more gold than the stamp mills and prompting the company to order a second pulverizer. When the

Engineering and Mining Journal

bottom of the crushing box wore out, however, it seemed like less of a bargain. The second Wiswell Pulverizer, with several improvements, was installed under the supervision of its inventor, but again wore out, costing $300 for repairs in a 46-day run. Both machines were abandoned, and the company continued its use of the old, reliable Cornish stamps.

In 1890, the Ropes company ordered a five-foot diameter Huntington centrifugal mill on approval. Rated at 15 tons per day, it was guaranteed to do the work of 10 stamps. Although this type of mill had been used with some success at the Michigan Gold Mine, it apparently didn't fulfill its promise at the Ropes, since it was never mentioned after being installed in July.

When the Fire Centre prospects closed down in 1893, that company's Crawford centrifugal ball mill was brought to the Ropes mine and given a trial run. Like the rock of the Dead River range, the hard quartz from the Ropes quickly wore the machine out.

Much of the gold in the Ropes mine is found in association with pyrite, which inhibits the amalgamation of gold with the mercury. The mill saved some of this ore by gravity concentration in Frue vanners, but shipping the gold-rich pyrite concentrate to Illinois for smelting cost $25 per ton, prompting the company to seek methods of treating it locally. Installation of a chlorination plant, in which the gold was released by roasting the ore and treating it with chlorine gas, was proposed in 1888 but never given a try. A smelting furnace was suggested several times and was tried on a small scale at the mine in 1890, using lead ores coming from the mine and other local prospects. Apparently it was not economically feasible to operate a smelter locally, since the concentrate continued to be shipped "below" for treatment.

As was the case with most mines of that day, a settlement had sprung up at the Ropes Gold Mine location. At first the miners were housed in a log boarding house, but starting in 1883 the company built a double row of houses on the north side of the valley for the miners and their families. The residents were

17

allowed free use of company land for pasturage, kept their own cows and planted gardens. In 1892, a company official proudly announced that the residents of the location had produced more than 1,000 bushels of potatoes.

A schoolhouse was built in 1886, and a school-

master and his wife, Mr. and Mrs. Irwin, joined the small community. Irwin was later replaced by Frank B. Wentworth. As part of a school district which included schools at the St. Lawrence Iron Mine and the Rock Kilns, the Ropes Gold Mine Public School served students from kindergarten through high school. On Sundays, church services were held in the schoolhouse.

The mine location was linked to town by a road along the Carp River to the Deer Lake Furnace. At first, the road was little more than a rough trail cut through the woods, passable for heavy loads only when frozen solid in the winter, but improvements were soon made. The road was corduroyed with

Miners' homes at the Ropes Gold Mine
Marquette County Historical Society

Ropes Gold Mine Public School
Kay Wallace Porter

cedar logs and filled with waste rock from the mine and slag from the Deer Lake Furnace. It eventually became a county highway. Stage service to the mine was inaugurated in the winter of 1884. John Burke, who ran the City Livery and Boarding Stables in Ishpeming, started the service with a horse-drawn sleigh, making two trips a day. A round trip took an hour and cost 75 cents.

For the first four years of the mine's operation, no power tools were used, all drilling being done by hand. Miners would work in three-man teams, "double jacking" — one man holding and turning the drill while the other two alternated hitting it with sledge hammers. Once a series of holes had been drilled, sticks of "giant powder" (as the new explosive we call dynamite was known) were tamped into place and touched off. The broken rock was loaded into tram cars by pick and shovel and pushed by hand

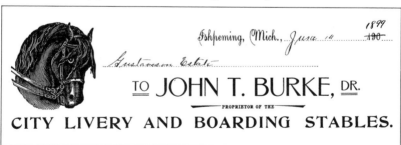

to the shaft where it was dumped into the skip. The shaft had been sunk 300 feet before power drills and the air compressor to run them were installed in 1886. Although this reduced the amount of hand labor, it also cost jobs, with the force of miners being cut from 30 to 12. Manual labor continued to be the only method of loading and tramming the ore, however.

The Ropes was considered to be a safe mine and compiled an enviable safety record for its era. Dur-

Commencement notice

Marie and Ensio Ostola

Negaunee Historical Society

19

ing the 14 years of its operation, only seven fatalities were recorded. A tragic record by today's standards, this was impressive when compared to the iron ore mines of that day where several fatalities per year were not unusual. The gold mine was in hard rock and needed no timbers to support the drifts and crosscuts, while the iron ore mines of that period were mining soft, earthy hematite ores which were prone to sudden caving.

Accidents did occur at the Ropes, however, as a result of both falling rock and primitive working conditions. The first fatality happened on September 8, 1886, when miner John H. Martin was working in the fourth level, west of the shaft. The 44-year-old Cornwall native was shoveling in a low stope when a piece of rock weighing two tons fell, killing him instantly. Two miners died by falling down the shaft in 1889. A Finnish miner, Robert Johnson, broke his neck when he fell 35 feet from a ladder on June 4. He died the following day in the Ishpeming hospital. On October 10, Gust Dalman died when he fell 350 feet. He had only been working in the mine for two months

"Double Jacking" — hand drilling underground
Superior View Studio

when he lost his footing while climbing rapidly down a ladder. The 19-year-old had been warned just that morning about his unsafe conduct on the shaft ladders. The accident which killed August Trakt, a trammer, in March 1890, was caused by the typically

primitive working conditions in the mine. After pushing a tram car of ore from a stope to the shaft, he was waiting for the skip when he slipped or lost his balance and fell into the unguarded shaft.

Ironically, the last three fatalities occurred during the final four months of the mine's operation. On March 23, 1897, trammer John Alio was dumping a tram car into the skip at the fifth level when the skip was hoisted unexpectedly. Alio, one of the oldest hands at the mine, was crushed between the skip and the shaft timbers. He died at the Ishpeming hospital two days later.

The final accident at the Ropes mine resulted in two deaths and may have precipitated the miners' suit which ultimately closed the mine. Two laborers were working in the deepest part of the mine, a 120-foot sinking stope below the 15th level. The area had been inspected by a foreman and declared safe, but about

Underground miners in the 1880s

Superior View Studio

21

a ton of rock broke loose from the roof and fell on Henry Oja and Abram Kylmanen, killing them instantly. The two men had been working at the mine only a short time, having immigrated from Finland just two months before. The accident occurred on June 21, 1897, and the mine closed down two weeks later. In each fatality a coroner's inquest was held, with the same verdict: accidental death, the company not at fault.

After the miners' suit forced its closing, the mine languished for a year in the hands of a receiver. Finally, Ishpeming postmaster Charles T. Fairbairn and attorney Albert K. Sedgwick took an option on the property. Fairbairn and Sedgwick brought the mine to the attention of several of the partners in the Michigan Copper Mining Company of Rockland, Michigan. These Detroit-based investors agreed to spend several thousand dollars to test the mine and drive a drift to a new vein west of the fifth level which had been found shortly before the mine closed. A small force of miners drifted into the vein from the fifth, seventh and 11th levels before the partners pulled out. Although the assays of the vein rock were satisfactory, there was apparently more profit to be made in the booming copper industry.

By 1899, creditors had given up hope for the mine's reopening. One of them, the Atlantic Dynamite Company, filed suit to recover the money it was owed. Circuit Court Judge J.W. Stone ordered the Ropes company's property sold at a receiver's sale on September 5, 1899. Frederick Braastad and Sven Johnson, who held a mortgage on the property, bought the mine for $2,500. The sale was set aside by the judge, however, since

Engineering and Mining Journal

the price was too low to cover the receiver's fee and the miners' and creditors' claims. A second sale on November 6 awarded the mine property to the Rand Drill Company of New York for $7,500. A month later the Rand company sold the mine to Corrigan, McKinney and Company, a Cleveland-based iron ore company, for $12,500.

Since the closing of the mine in 1897, introduction of the cyanide leaching process had revitalized the gold mining industry in the American West. Cyanide could liberate the fine particles of gold which could not be recovered by amalgamation and which were inefficiently saved by gravity concentration. Tests performed on the Ropes mine tailings indicated that there were about 100,000 tons of tailings which could yield one dollar per ton profit under cyanide treatment, so Corrigan, McKinney and Company, under the direction of J. Forrest Orr and John L. Malm, erected five redwood leaching tanks, each 40 feet in diameter and 10 feet deep, along with 15 smaller intermediate and precipitation tanks. Tailings were hauled to and from the tanks in one-ton tram cars. Operating through the warm months of 1900 and 1901, the plant extracted a reported $54,682 in gold and silver from 30,000 tons of tailings, although in later years Leverett Ropes, son of Julius Ropes, reported that he had private information that the actual amount recovered was $194,000. William H. Rood, president of the Deer Lake Iron Company and the former manager of the Ropes mine, also set up vats to leach tailings which had washed onto the Deer Lake Company's lands. Corrigan, McKinney and Company obtained an injunction to stop Rood from working, claiming ownership of the tailings. The injunction was overturned in court, however, and Rood treated tailings for part of a season, recovering an undisclosed quantity of gold before his death in May 1902.

Another unexpected bonus came when Malm inspected the old mill building, where he found discarded amalgamation plates holding a considerable amount of gold. Some of the plates had been cleaned only on the front, leaving precious amalgam on the

Frank Lundin with
Ropes gold ore
Superior View Studio

back side. On other plates the copper had been eaten away and replaced by gold-mercury amalgam. The inexperience of the Ropes company's mill men was shown by the fact that some $30,000 was recovered from these supposedly worthless plates.

Corrigan, McKinney and Company never reopened the underground workings of the Ropes mine, but finally sold the mill machinery and the 24 buildings on the property to William and Albert Trebilcock of Ishpeming. While tearing down the mill buildings for the lumber, the brothers found considerable amalgam under the floor, enough to bring in more money than the sale of the scrap lumber.

A pair of Ishpeming men, Frank Lundin and Albert Bjork, acquired a lease on the Ropes property in 1927. By setting up sluice boxes and siphoning water from the shaft, they were able to recover $1,000 worth of gold and silver amalgam from beneath the old stamp and vanner rooms.

In 1932, Bjork and Lundin were joined by James and William Trebilcock, Abel Niemi and James E. Flaa in forming the Ishpeming Gold Mining Company. Bjork, an Ishpeming businessman, served as president of the company. Lundin, a National Mine resident who had mined gold in Alaska, served as vice president and treasurer. The company reprocessed some 200 tons of tailings from an untouched portion of the tailings pile with the aid of four students from the Michigan College of Mining and Technology in Houghton. Using cyanide leaching, they recovered 9.67 ounces of gold and 14 ounces of silver, valued at $247. The same year, Bjork and Lundin leased 320 acres in Section 30, south and west of the former

Phillips gold property, and explored for additional veins. On the NW ¼ of the SE ¼ of the section, they found a promising quartz vein which they traced more than 500 feet. The vein was followed by digging trenches and test pits, and a small shaft was sunk at one point, apparently without finding pay rock.

In 1934, when the government-controlled price of

gold was raised from $20.67 to $35 per ounce, the Calumet and Hecla Consolidated Copper Company bought an 85 percent interest in the company for $30,000. C&H brought in equipment and miners from their copper mining properties in Calumet, repaired the old captain's house for the miners and dewatered the mine, pumping out about 23 million gallons of water. A headframe from the Phoenix Copper Mine and a hoist and air compressor from the Republic Iron Mine were installed at the shaft. The 800-foot level was extended 300 feet to the east, and a new drift was driven 800 feet west of the shaft on the same level. Samples were taken every foot and crosscuts made every 50 feet. The ore was hauled out of the mine in blasting powder boxes and sent to the Hollinger Mine in Porcupine, Ontario, for a mill run to confirm the results of assays made by C&H.

The company also explored by diamond drill, both

Miners at the Ropes Gold Mine, 1935

Superior View Studio

from the surface and from the ninth, 13th and 15th levels underground. These tests found reserves of 1.5 million tons of ore averaging .14 ounce of gold per ton, showing the mineralized zone to extend to a depth of at least 1,600 feet. Underground testing was completed in the summer of 1936, but the mine was kept pumped out.

In 1941, Calumet and Hecla acquired the rest of the outstanding stock in the Ishpeming Gold Mining Company and purchased the mineral rights from Republic Steel, Corrigan McKinney's successor. The company was considering reopening the mine with a new shaft and modern mill in 1942. But the War Production Board ordered all gold mines shut down to allow miners to work in the strategically important copper mines.

The property was sold by Calumet and Hecla in 1957 to two Ishpeming men, real estate agent Joe Paul and lawyer Edmund Thomas, who resold it a few months later to Arcadian Copper Mine Tours of Ripley, Michigan. Arcadian planned to open the mine as a tourist attraction by driving a horizontal adit into the third level. Their plan was never carried out.

When the government abandoned the gold standard in 1971, the price of gold rose dramatically, eventually reaching more than $800 an ounce. These inflated gold prices made many previously marginal or unprofitable gold mines attractive to mining companies across the country. A Marquette firm, Resource Exploration Incorporated, initiated an evaluation program on the gold prospects in Marquette County, concentrating on the Ropes as the most favorable. They presented their findings to a number of mining companies, and in January 1975 the Ropes mine was sold to Callahan Mining Corporation of Phoenix, Arizona, for about $60,000. Calla-

Ropes Gold Mine, 1935
Superior View Studio

26

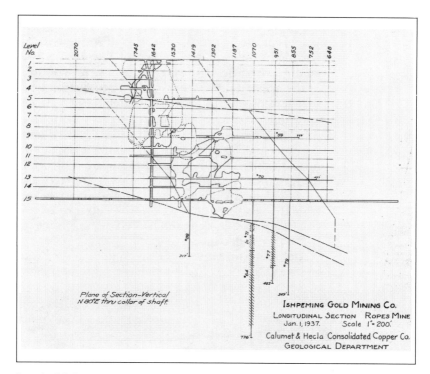

Level No.

Plane of Section–Vertical
N 80°E thru collar of shaft

ISHPEMING GOLD MINING CO.
LONGITUDINAL SECTION   ROPES MINE
Jan. 1, 1937.   Scale 1"= 200'.
Calumet & Hecla Consolidated Copper Co.
GEOLOGICAL DEPARTMENT

han held the property in reserve until the rising price of gold in 1979 prompted an exploration and evaluation program, initially involving geophysical and geochemical studies and the mapping of surface outcrops. The next phase of the exploration involved diamond drilling from the surface to determine the extent and richness of the gold-bearing rock.

In August 1980, pumps were installed to dewater the mine and a headframe and hoist were installed at the Curry shaft. The 400- and 800-foot levels of the mine were rehabilitated and extensive diamond drilling was carried out to detail the ore body. A bulk sample was excavated and shipped to Michigan Technological University for testing and developing an appropriate concentrating process. Total cost for these preliminary steps was $2.5 million.

In July 1983 a contract was awarded to Wallace Diamond Mining Incorporated of Osborne, Idaho (since reorganized as Fausett Mine Services), to sink a spiral

Sectional view of Ropes Gold Mine, 1937
Resource Exploration Inc.

ramp to the 500-foot level and, on July 25, 1983, 100 years after the first run of the original Ropes mill, the sinking of the new decline began. The decline was continued to a depth of 900 feet, below the workings of the original mine. Here the first production level was developed. The ore body, which is up to 70 feet wide and extends 1,100 feet to the east, was undermined along its entire length. At the eastern end, raises were driven between the mining levels at 800 feet and above. Six-inch blast holes were drilled and charged from the mining levels, and the ore was blasted down into the undercut and raises. At first, the ore from this stope was loaded via crosscuts into 26-ton trucks in a parallel drift and hauled to the surface up the 1½-mile decline.

Although sinking a decline is an inexpensive way to open a mine, truck haulage is a very inefficient

Underground haulage truck entering the portal of the decline

Daniel Fountain

method of raising the ore. A decision was made in 1984 to excavate a vertical shaft and to install a hoist and headframe acquired from the Lakeshore Copper Mine near Casa Grande, Arizona. Rather than sinking the shaft from the surface, Callahan decided to open it by backreaming. A 12-inch pilot hole was drilled from the surface to a room which had been excavated at the 1,050-foot level south of the ore zone. A gigantic reaming tool was then assembled in the room and slowly hoisted toward the surface, drilling out the rock as it went and leaving a 14-foot diameter, untimbered shaft. Although the shaft and associated equipment cost $3.8 million, it was estimated that a $35-per-ounce saving could be realized by hoisting rather than trucking the ore to the surface. Equipment was still driven in and out of the mine via the decline, but the ore was hoisted up the shaft in 15-ton capacity skips.

As the ore above the 900-foot level was depleted, the decline was extended, with draw levels being developed at the 1,284- and 1,548-foot levels. Ore was mined from a stope extending up to the 1,020-foot level much as it was from the upper levels in the mine. The decline was continued still deeper, heading toward an ore body beginning at a depth of about 2,000 feet. Diamond drilling has shown the ore in this zone to be comparable in width and richness to that in the upper levels.

From the mine, the ore was trucked some 15 miles to Humboldt, where Callahan had purchased and renovated the former Humboldt Mining Company iron ore concentrator. Part of the trip was made over a new road constructed on an old railroad grade between North Lake and the Verde Antique marble quarry just west of the gold mine.

Utilization of modern milling and recovery techniques allowed Callahan to profitably treat ore that had been uneconomical for the original operators of the mine. While the amalgamation and gravity concentration methods used by the miners of the past century could only recover the coarser gold from the quartz vein rock, the modern chemical process could

Ropes headframe
Daniel Fountain

treat all of the rock, vein quartz and greenstone country rock alike.

At the Humboldt plant, the coarse ore from the mine was crushed in two stages and fed to two 10½-foot diameter by 16-foot-long ball mills for fine grinding. A ball mill uses a rotating drum partially filled with hard steel balls to grind the ore. Xanthate, a flotation reagent, was added to the finely ground ore, and air was bubbled through the mixture. The gold, along with its associated pyrite and copper minerals, would cling to the air bubbles and float to the top, leaving the waste rock behind. After more gold-bearing minerals were floated off in two additional flotation stages, the waste rock tailings were piped to the flooded Humboldt mine pit for disposal. The gold-bearing flotation concentrate was ground to a finer consistency in a 10-foot diameter, 6-foot-long regrind ball mill, then dewatered in a bank of vacuum disc filters. Next, it was mixed with a dilute solution of sodium cyanide and aerated for 24 to 48 hours until the gold and silver were leached out of the ore. The gold-bearing cyanide solution was separated from the concentrate in vacuum drum filters. The concentrate was then mixed with fresh cyanide, and the leaching and filtering process was repeated to recover additional gold and silver values. After the gold-bearing cyanide solution was clarified and de-aerated, powdered zinc was added, causing the gold to precipitate out of solution. This precipitate, which contained gold and silver along with traces of other metals, was finally melted down and cast into buttons of doré bullion. The bullion was sold to refineries for further purification.

Downhole drilling on 800-foot level of Ropes Gold Mine
Daniel Fountain

30

Once the gold was leached out of the concentrate, copper, silver and pyrite were left in the concentrate.

These minerals were separated out in two more stages of flotation and dried. The resulting copper/silver/pyrite concentrate was sold to the Copper Range Mining Company's White Pine copper smelter, where it was added to the smelter feed, both to recover some of the silver and copper values and to act as a flux.

Mining today is generally much safer than it was

Underground haulage truck at Ropes
Daniel Fountain

Primary ball mill at Callahan's Humboldt plant
Daniel Fountain

100 years ago, due to federal mining laws, company safety policies and the use of machinery in place of manpower. Despite these improvements, underground mining continues to be a hazardous occupation, and the modern Ropes mine has had its share of accidents. On June 4, 1987, a miner was operating a jumbo drill rig in the haulage level 1,284 feet below

surface. Suddenly, a large mass of rock let go from the roof and fell on the jumbo, partially burying it and caving in part of the protective canopy over the operator's compartment. Fortunately, the operator escaped injury. Nine days later, however, another miner was not so lucky. While he and his partner were installing rock bolts in an attempt to secure some unstable ground at the 1,154-foot level, some rock broke loose and fell. The falling rock knocked the miner down and buried him to his waist, breaking his left leg in several places. Another miner was injured by falling rock on August 29, 1987. The miner was installing roof bolts in an unstable area on the 420-foot level when some loose rock fell, breaking both of his feet.

Flotation cells and leach tanks at Humboldt
Daniel Fountain

The most dramatic accident at the Ropes mine occurred on the morning of December 31, 1987. Shortly after the day shift arrived at work, surface workers heard a rumbling noise, dust began to spew from the Curry shaft and the ground near the shaft began to cave in. Although the production stope of the modern mine began at a depth of 300 feet and went down to 900 feet, the first level of the old mine was only 30 feet below the surface. The original miners had mined out the upper levels of the mine, leaving great open stopes reaching from the first level to at least the fifth level at 250 feet. As the ore body in the modern stope was mined out up to the 300-foot level, the pillar of rock between the old and new stopes was left unsupported. When it finally collapsed into the stope, the old workings, honeycombed with drifts, crosscuts and stopes, caved in with it.

As the employees watched the gaping hole grow, a delivery man bringing supplies to the mine began to drive in the entrance road toward the shafthouse and the mine buildings beyond. The mine workers stopped the driver and told him to back up. The driver parked his van and was waiting for permission to enter when the ground gave way beneath the truck, plunging him into the collapsing mine. Stunned and bleeding, he struggled out of his truck and scrambled to safety up the side of the still-crumbling cave-in.

Drum and disc filters
Daniel Fountain

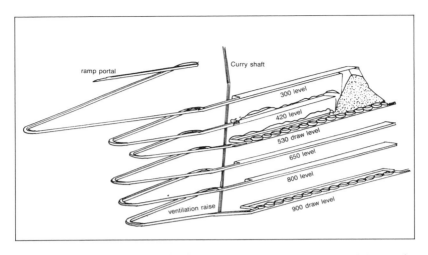

Fortunately, his injuries were minor, requiring only a few stitches. Nobody else was injured, but a power

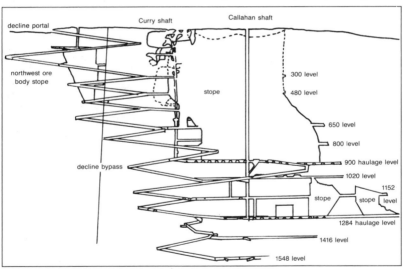

Isometric drawing of Ropes project
Skillings Mining Magazine

Ropes Gold Mine sectional view, 1980s
Daniel Fountain collection

line, the mine geologist's office and the Curry shaft-house were swallowed up in the 200-by-700-foot long, 100-foot-deep hole.

The cave-in did not damage Callahan's production shaft, which is located about 200 feet south of the stope. The shaft was rendered unusable for several days, though, since the power line supplying the hoist was lost in the cave-in. Once power was restored, company officials and federal mine inspectors were able to inspect the mine. They found no damage to the working areas of the mine, but, due to safety considerations, it was about two months before full production could be resumed.

In order to stabilize the ground surrounding the caved stope, Callahan had 350,000 cubic yards of sand trucked in and dumped into the hole. Until the

stope was filled, no ore could be mined from the production levels at 900 feet and below. Low grade ore from stockpiles at the mine was processed at the plant, along with higher grade ore from a small ore body northwest of the main workings. This ore was mined from a crosscut from the decline and trucked to the surface. To provide safe access to the levels below the 900-foot production level, an alternate leg was added to the decline, running from the 900-foot level down to the 1,020-foot level.

Although the cave-in was an expensive accident for Callahan, it did have one potential benefit. The original plan for the mine called for ore to be pulled from the bottom of the stope as it was blasted loose, leaving a great empty hole along the ore zone. Early on

1887 mill building
Marquette County Historical Society

35

Scenes near
Ropes Gold Mine
*Michigan History
Magazine*

it was discovered that the wall rock surrounding the gold ore was not strong enough to stand on its own. The sides of the stope began to cave in, diluting the

1884 (left) and
1887 (right) mill
buildings
*Marquette County
Historical Society*

gold ore with worthless rock. To support the stope walls, production was halted for a month in the spring of 1986 while ore in the upper levels was blasted loose to fill the stope. To avoid similar problems in the lower levels, a pillar of ore was to be left

36

between the 900-foot production level and next stope being developed from 1,020 to 1,548 feet. Once the upper stope caved in, it became possible to change the mining system to one of continuous caving, backfilling the stope from the surface as ore was pulled from the bottom. With the entire stope stabilized with fill, the pillar of ore between 900 and 1,020 feet could be blasted loose and recovered.

In October 1989, Callahan announced the indefinite shutdown of the Ropes mine. An unstable zone of rock where the gold-bearing formation meets the surrounding country rock was threatening to allow a section of the untimbered shaft to collapse. The low grade of ore the mine had been producing and the price of gold were undoubtedly also factors in the closing. Original projections for the mine were that the ore would average one ounce of gold per 10 tons of ore. When it was shut down, however, it had been yielding only an ounce for every 17 tons milled. The price of gold, which was at $324 per ounce when the mine opened, had risen to $450 by early 1987, the mine's most profitable year. The price had fallen to $366 when the shutdown was announced.

Hoisting was stopped in October to allow the com-

ROPES GOLD AND SILVER COMPANY PRODUCTION 1883-1897

YEAR	TONS	GOLD	SILVER	PRODUCTION	YIELD/TON
1883	272	$1,651.16	$358.81	$2,009.97	$7.39
1884	1,371	$6,163.19	$616.20	$6,779.39	$4.94
1885	5,643	$23,288.92	$2,942.19	$26,231.11	$4.65
1886	6,959	$38,499.93	$4,653.92	$43,153.85	$6.20
1887	10,216	$32,338.63	$2,592.03	$34,930.66	$3.42
1888	16,855	$52,353.94	$5,330.81	$57,684.75	$3.42
1889	31,365	$90,060.40	$9,655.05	$99,715.45	$3.18
1890	31,578	$71,132.70	$8,435.57	$79,568.27	$2.52
1891	21,355	$63,760.59	$8,025.39	$71,785.98	$3.36
1892	21,794	$52,443.08	$7,160.82	$59,603.90	$2.73
1893	15,080	$40,416.56	$3,509.21	$43,925.77	$2.91
1894	21,185	$43,676.77	$1,789.00	$45,465.77	$2.15
1895	16,535*	$34,838.69	$1,373.16	$36,211.85	$2.19
1896	16,686	$37, 235.98*	$1,489.44*	$38,845.42	$2.32
1897	Figures not available				
TOTAL	216,894	$587,860.54	$57,931.60	$645,792.14	$2.98

*Estimated

pany to reinforce the shaft. Three hundred fifty feet of the shaft in the unstable zone was to be lined with steel and grouted with concrete. Bids for the reinforcement work came in too high, however, and Callahan decided on a contingency plan to allow operation of the mine if economic conditions improved. Rather than reinforce the unstable portion of the shaft, which was in the deeper reaches of the mine, the company decided to abandon the lower portion of the shaft and truck ore part way up the decline to the original skip loading pocket at the 900-foot level. To provide the necessary alternate escape route formerly provided by the shaft, raises were excavated between the decline legs in the lower levels of the mine. Gold prices failed to rise sufficiently, however, and in April 1990 Callahan Mining Corporation announced that the Ropes mine and mill were being put in mothballs. In the spring of 1991, mining equipment, including dewatering pumps and the underground primary crusher, were removed, and the mine was left to slowly fill with water. The mining equipment, haulage trucks and mine hoist, as well as the Humboldt processing plant, were put up for sale ending another chapter in the gold mining history of Michigan.

CHAPTER TWO

The Michigan Gold Mine

Anson B. Miner, the cashier at the Ishpeming National Bank, had lived in the West for several years and was familiar with gold prospecting. With the Ropes gold mine coming into its own in 1885, Miner and several companions spent their spare time searching for other gold veins. One vein of rusty looking, yellow-stained quartz some three miles west of the Ropes caught his eye. On Sunday, June 14, 1885, Miner and his partners set off a blast in this vein which broke out a large quantity of quartz with glittering particles of gold protruding from the rock. Miner's group tried to get a lease on the land from its owner, the Lake Superior Iron Company, but a company policy forbade the granting of leases for mineral exploration. Unable to pursue their find on the iron company's land, the prospectors followed the vein a quarter mile to the east onto private land on the NW ¼ of the NE ¼ of Section 35, T48N-R28W. The landowner, Peter Gingrass, who ran Ishpeming's Urban House hotel, was more than happy to grant the prospectors a lease on his forty — for a price. The Miner partnership, which included bank director Edward R. Hall, iron mining agent James Jopling, assayer Will L. Jones and W.L. Lyons, immediately sold an interest in the property to Peter White, pioneer businessman of Marquette, and started sinking a shaft. About this time it became known that Gingrass had granted an earlier option to Joseph C. Foley, but had subsequently refused him a lease, due

to his lack of progress in exploring the land.

Interest in the property lagged for two years until gold-bearing quartz worth $44,000 per ton was discovered in the adjacent Lake Superior Iron Company's shaft in July 1887. Within a week, Foley set a crew of men to work crosscutting the vein, but Miner, accompanied by Peter White's lawyers, evicted Foley's men and set up a camp of his own, a move characterized in a local newspaper as "claim jumping."

By this time, a group of Cleveland iron and steel industrialists, headed by Colonel James Pickands and Samuel Mather of the powerful iron ore mining company Pickands, Mather and Company, had bought the Miner and White lease and formed the Michigan Gold Company. The company renegotiated the lease with Gingrass and extended it to 40 years for an immediate payment of $10,000 and a 10 percent royalty. Frank P. Mills, the superintendent of the Cleveland Iron Mine, was put in charge of the Michigan Gold Company's property.

A third claimant, George Grummett of Ishpeming, entered the fray by having the five men working for the Michigan company as well as Foley's two men arrested. Grummett, who was backed by Captain William Ward of Pittsburgh, claimed to have a lease on the property from Gingrass, but its validity was questionable. The arrest of the Michigan and Foley parties was thrown out by Justice of the Peace Leonard P. Crary of Marquette, but Grummett was able to make a second arrest stick, with the men being fined $10 each by Justice of the Peace Stearnes of Clarksburg.

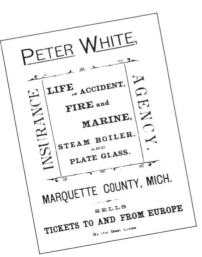

Ishpeming City Directory, 1894

Marquette City Directory

40

Not coincidentally, the settlement and blast furnace at Clarksburg were owned in part by the Ward family. In October, the powerful Michigan company had Grummett and his superintendent, William Gardiner, arrested and evicted, effectively gaining control of

the property. The Michigan company built a boarding house and sank two shafts, the No. 1 to 76 feet and the No. 2 to 40 feet, before suspending operations for the winter in January.

The spring of 1888 found the Michigan company reopening and dewatering its shafts on the gold range, and defending itself against a lawsuit by Grummett in the courts at Marquette. Work on the property was limited to exploration and prospecting pending the outcome of the lawsuit. In August, Judicial Court Judge C.B. Grant delivered a decision in favor of the Michigan Gold Company, but work was still held to a minimum because of an appeal to the state Supreme Court by Grummett and Ward. Grummett, meanwhile, was sinking a shaft on another vein half a mile to the east.

The true nature of the Michigan mine became apparent in late August when a rich lode of quartz was

Michigan Gold Company stock
Peter White Public Library

found near the surface in the No. 2 shaft. Pieces of rock the size of walnuts were found that carried up to 1.5 ounces of gold, and pieces of shattered quartz were held together by the soft, flexible native metal. Assays of the rock showed as much as $100,000 worth of gold per ton. This rich lode was followed to a depth of 50 feet by the end of 1888.

In January 1889, 70 tons of rock from the Michigan mine were run through the stamp mills of the Ropes Gold and Silver Company. The ore proved to be easily crushed and yielded $6.68 per ton. Rich specimens continued to be found in the several shafts as the Michigan company awaited the Supreme Court's decision. Finally, on November 8, 1889, the Michigan Supreme Court handed down a decision in favor of the Michigan company, and within two weeks, the company installed boilers, steam engines and a hoisting plant. Mining began in earnest.

In a demonstration of the potential yield of the mine, about 200 pounds of rock were brought to Ishpeming, coarsely crushed and washed in a hand rocker. Even by these crude concentrating methods, 137 ounces of gold were extracted, a yield of $30,000 per ton. The gold was cast into two bricks, each 8-by-2-by-.5-inch, and put on public display. With this proof and the company's clear title to the mine, Michigan Gold Company stock skyrocketed, increasing 500 percent in one 10-day period. A force of 18 men went to work, continuing to sink the valuable No. 2 shaft. They also erected a mill building housing a Blake jaw crusher and secondary roll crusher, which fed a 3½-foot Huntington centrifugal grinding mill. The company's intention was to mill the rich

Frank P. Mills, the Michigan Gold Company's superintendent
Daniel Fountain collection

rock as it was mined to cover expenses until the extent of the gold deposit was known and a permanent stamp mill of an appropriate size could be erected. However, the mill and its associated equipment didn't run as smoothly as expected, because the mill was too small. As a result, the company had to call in a 10-cent-per-share assessment in May 1890 to cover expenses. Typical production costs for milling the rock from shaft sinking and drifting was $12 to $24 per ton.

The mining company also underwent a change of management in May, the Cleveland directors giving way to Upper Peninsula influence. David M. Ford, a prosperous stockbroker, and James R. Cooper, the superintendent of the Calumet and Hecla copper smelter, both of Houghton, were elected to the board. They were joined by Peter White of Marquette, the famous iron mining captain Samuel L. Mitchell of Negaunee and Ishpeming merchant A.W. Myers.

The Michigan mine's managers had long suspected that some of the miners were "high grading," that is, stealing valuable specimens of gold. Miners would work for a few months, secretly carrying out hundreds of dollars worth of gold in their lunch pails, then suddenly quit and leave town. In May 1890, a pair of such "high graders" was arrested on the eve of their departure for England. Henry Varcoe, who had been a shift boss at the mine, and his son, William, were caught with more than 200 pounds of rich quartz in their steamer trunks, estimated to be worth anywhere from $1,000 to $5,000. The next day,

Engineering and Mining Journal

William Uren, who ran the boardinghouse at the mine, was arrested when several ounces of coarse gold were found in his possession. The mining company was unable to prove in court that either the Varcoes' or Uren's gold came from the Michigan mine, however, and all three were acquitted. The mining company instituted tighter controls on its miners and erected a barbed wire fence surrounding the entire length of the vein.

Rich specimens notwithstanding, the total supply of gold at the Michigan mine remained in doubt, prompting the company to make another test run of low grade rock at the Ropes mill in September 1890. The run yielded only $2.82 per ton, indicating that the high grade rock had pinched out. Another 10-cent-per-share assessment was called to provide capital to install an air compressor and power drills and to sink the shaft farther in search of more rich deposits. In February 1891, a third mill test of 1,000 tons was ordered at the Ropes. However, the yield from the tested rock was so low (at 71 cents per ton) that the test was stopped after only half that amount had been stamped.

The Michigan Gold Company then hired the Ropes company's manager William H. Rood and superintendent George Weatherston to systematically sample and test the various veins and openings on the property. After nearly a month, Rood and Weatherston submitted their report, having found an average of less than a dollar per ton in shafts 1, 2 and 3. Only the vein found at the No. 4 shaft and at a small shaft nearby was considered worth mining. Accordingly, the company moved its portable hoist to the No. 4 shaft, dewatered it and continued sinking. A rich seam of pay rock produced

$1,000 per month for a few months, enough to cover expenses.

During 1892, 15 cents per share in assessments was called to provide operating capital for a reduced force of miners. It was decided that a surface crew of seven men to support only four miners was too expensive, since it cost the company $53 per foot of drifting. The company took bids on a contract for hand-powered drifting, estimating that a two-thirds saving could be realized.

Although another valuable streak was found near the No. 3 shaft and a new small vein was found to the south, the mine was shut down for the winter in January 1893. However, the mine wasn't reopened in the spring as planned. Although the workings were pumped out in late-June, unfavorable economic conditions brought on by the Panic of 1893 prompted company president Peter White to decide against the resumption of mining. The management still had faith in the property, though, since the company renewed its option that summer and talked of putting in a five-stamp mill.

Ishpeming City Directory 1891 (Gazetteer of Marquette County 1889)

The mine was still idle in the summer of 1894 when Thomas Trevithic, the former mining captain, brought specimens of quartz with native gold assaying $150,000 per ton to the company's attention,

Peter White
Daniel Fountain collection

claiming to have found a new vein on the Michigan property. He offered to reveal the location of the vein for a fee of $250 and the promise of six months work, but, distrusting the company (and Peter White in particular), later raised his price to $1,000. The company chose not to pay him, but set several of its own men to work prospecting for more rich veins. Enough

pay rock was found to keep the mine working intermittently until January 1896 when the Michigan Gold Company shut down for good. Total reported production was $17,699.36, although an unknown amount in rich specimens had also been stolen from the mine and ore piles.

In 1901, Peter Gingrass, the owner of the Michigan property, approached several groups of investors in the Copper Country in an attempt to reopen the mine. He gave an option to Will A. Bateman of Calumet and L.C. Fredericks of Colorado, but no work was done. Another attempt to reopen the mine was made in 1902 by Gingrass' son-in-law, Edward Copps, who had been an officer of the Wakefield Gold and Silver Company during the Wakefield gold mining boom in 1887. Copps tried unsuccessfully to raise $25,000 to incorporate the Pere Marquette Mining Company to work the Michigan mine. The next year,

Ishpeming City Directory

however, he did persuade the Tribullion Mining, Smelting and Development Company, which had mining properties in Arizona and Montana, to lease

the property and conduct explorations.

The Tribullion company dewatered the old No. 1 and 2 shafts, finding rich quartz in both shafts and in the drift between them. The drift was extended to the east over the next few months until, in December 1903, the air compressor supplying the power

Michigan Gold Mine in 1905
Marquette County Historical Society

Michigan Gold Mine in 1935
Superior View Studio

47

drills broke down. Even though they were finding rich quartz, company officials decided to allow their lease to lapse in order to concentrate their efforts on their copper mines in the west.

Although the rich pockets of gold were elusive, the abundant white quartz had economic value of its own. When finely ground and screened, it sold for $18 to $40 per ton, being useful as a filler and abrasive. Seeing the possibility of mining quartz for sale as silica while still seeking rich pockets of gold, Edward Copps and his associates formed the Ishpeming Gold Mines Company in 1905. Copps served as president of the new company, with E.D. Nelson, a former Ishpeming resident who had become a prominent banker in Iron River, as vice president, Peter Gingrass' son Joseph as the secretary and William Noon of Marquette as treasurer. Other directors included Peter White, Otto Eger of Ishpeming and George Russell, a successful banker from Detroit. The company bought the Michigan, Peninsular, Superior and Grummett gold properties from Gingrass for $25,000 and began development work at the Michigan mine.

Over the next few years, the Ishpeming Gold Mines Company reopened two of the shafts, built a mill building and installed the equipment necessary to grind the quartz and separate any precious metals or

Miners at the
Michigan Gold
Mine in the 1930s
Ethel Valenzio

impurities before shipping the silica powder. The mine and mill finally went into operation in the summer of 1908.

Quartz was mined from the No. 2 shaft and taken from the dumps left from earlier operations. After crushing, the ore was fed to a Huntington centrifugal mill, which ground the quartz and separated some of the coarse gold. More gold was separated from the

ore on vibrating tables, and iron and other heavy minerals were removed in a Frue vanner. The pure quartz was then finely ground in a tube mill, dried and barreled for shipment.

The mine was sold in 1909 to the Michigan Quartz Silica Company. This Milwaukee-based company, of which Copps was also an officer, operated the property intermittently for the next few years. The Milwaukee company eventually shut down the Michigan operation, finding it less expensive to buy quartz from Wisconsin and Illinois and treat it in its mill in Milwaukee.

Miners at the Michigan Gold Mine in 1935
Superior View Studio

49

The mine did not attract any further attention until 1933, when a group of investors formed Michigan Gold Mines Incorporated. These investors, led by Henry B. King of Three Rivers, president, Wesley B. Orr of Manistique, vice president, Frank Trombley of Marquette, treasurer, and Cora Secor of Gladwin, secretary, leased the Michigan mine and shipped 10 tons of rock from the mine dump to the Michigan College of Mining and Technology for testing. The new company erected a headframe at the No. 4 shaft and started sinking below its original depth of 53 feet. Within a few feet, the "pinched out" vein opened out to five feet wide. The shaft was deepened to 270 feet, and 1,000 feet of drifting and development work was carried out on the 150- and 250-foot levels. A mill building was also erected, in which the ore was processed by first crushing it in a jaw crusher, then finely grinding it in a 72-by-36-inch Hardinge ball mill. The gold was separated from the rock by gravity concentration on corduroy blankets, then amalgamated with mercury. The first shipment of bullion, consisting of a brick weighing 18 ounces, was made in April 1934.

Miners at the
Michigan Gold
Mine in the 1930s
Ethel Valenzio

The value of the gold produced was enhanced by the 1934 increase in the statutory price from $20.67 to $35 per ounce.

During the summer of 1934, the Michigan College of Mines held a mill practice course at the Michigan mine, experimenting with methods for extracting

gold from the ore. Four shipments of bullion were made to the U.S. Mint in New York that year, totaling 58.63 ounces. In May 1935, the company was reorganized as the Michigan Gold Mining Company. Henry B. King stayed on as the president and general manager and Samuel M. Cohodas of Ishpeming joined as vice president. The rest of the directors came from Milwaukee and the Appleton area of Wisconsin, including A.F. Schroeder, treasurer; Clarence F. Manser, secretary; Walter L. Schroeder and Dr. J.G. LaHam. K. Spiroff of the Michigan College of Mining and Technology in Houghton served as consulting engineer for the company.

Michigan Gold Mining Company stock certificate
Daniel Fountain collection

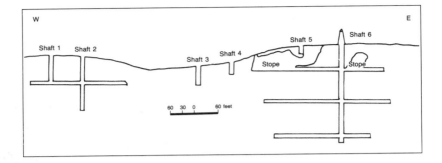

No mining or milling was done in 1935 and 1936 while exploration and development work was carried out underground and a 100-ton flotation plant was installed on the surface. The mill ran for a few months in 1937, but only produced 51 ounces of gold, worth about $1,800. The company then shut down, leaving the miners unpaid when one of the company officials reportedly absconded with all the gold recovered from the mill in the final cleanup. The following year, a bolt of lightning struck the power lines leading to the mine, burning out the electric motors in the mill. The company was reorganized once again late in 1939, this time as Marquette Mines Incorporated. The new company paid off the mine's outstanding debts, but never reopened the property.

The renewed interest in the Ishpeming Gold Range in the 1970s and '80s extended to the Michigan mine, which was included in the preliminary studies leading up to the purchase of the Ropes Gold Mine by Callahan Mining Corporation. The Michigan property was purchased by Callahan in 1985, raising hopes that this one-time bonanza would once again be profitably mined.

Sectional view of the Michigan Gold Mine

Strategic Minerals Investigations in Marquette and Baraga Counties, 1943

CHAPTER THREE

Michigan Range Prospects

A lthough the Ropes mine proved that gold could be found in Michigan, it was the rich finds at the Lake Superior Mine which brought national attention to the Ishpeming Gold Range. In July 1885, prospectors discovered gold on the NE ¼ of the NW ¼ of Section 35, T48N-R28W, owned by the Lake Superior Iron Company. Since the mining company would not grant mineral leases, the explorers followed the vein onto land owned by a private individual, where the Michigan Gold Mine was eventually started.

The Lake Superior Company, which owned and operated several large iron ore mines in Ishpeming, was less than enthusiastic about gold mining, especially since the company president, James S. Fay of Boston, had lost money in an ill-advised gold mining venture in Colorado. The company planned to test the vein by diamond drilling, but their drill rigs were in constant use exploring for iron ore. Finally in June 1887, an exploratory shaft was started. It had been sunk on the vein to a depth of 22 feet when an eight-inch rich streak was found, holding up to $44,000 per ton in gold and silver. The rock was so filled with gold that large chunks of shattered quartz were held together by the soft, flexible metal.

News of the rich find traveled quickly, being broadcast as far away as New York. The Lake Superior Company temporarily closed off the shaft, posted a guard and built a stockade around the stockpile. Organized

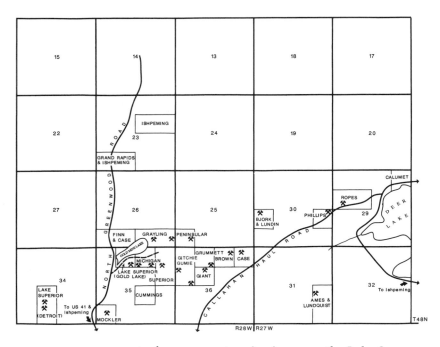

The Michigan
Gold Range
NMU Cartographic Lab

Map labels: 15, 14, 13, 18, 17 / 22, ISHPEMING, 23, GRAND RAPIDS & ISHPEMING, 24, 19, 20 / 27, GREENWOOD ROAD, 26, 25, BJORK & LUNDIN, 30, PHILLIPS, ROPES, CALUMET, DEER LAKE, 29 / FINN & CASE, GRAYLING, PENINSULAR, GITCHIE GUMIE, GRUMMETT, BROWN, CASE, GIANT, MICHIGAN, LAKE SUPERIOR (GOLD LAKE), SUPERIOR, NORTH GREENWOOD ROAD, GOLD MINE LAKE, HAUL ROAD, CALLAHAN HAUL ROAD / 34, LAKE SUPERIOR, To US 41 & Ishpeming, (DETROIT), 35, CUMMINGS, MOCKLER, 36, 31, AMES & LUNDQUIST, 32, To Ishpeming, R28W R27W, T48N

as a stock company to mine iron ore, the Lake Superior Iron Company had to reorganize its charter to go into the gold mining business.

With their legal position secured, the company continued to explore, sinking a 25-foot shaft on a second vein 100 feet to the south. In the spring of 1888, the main shaft was dewatered and enlarged under the supervision of Captain John Jenkins, and a steam hoisting plant was installed. More rich rock was found at 35 feet, assaying as high as $60,000 per ton. The shaft was deepened to 100 feet over the next year, and drifts were driven at the 40- and 100-foot levels, but no more rich streaks were found. The quartz in the lower reaches of the mine still averaged $6 per ton, however. The majority of the company's stockholders remained opposed to the relatively speculative business of gold mining, and at the June 19, 1889, stockholders' meeting in Boston, they voted to sell or lease the gold prospect to outside developers. Operations at the shaft ceased two months later.

Four months after the Lake Superior Company shut

down operations, the Gold Lake Mining Company was formed to operate the mine. Officers included George W. Hayden of Ishpeming, president; N.H. Stewart of Kalamazoo, vice president; Charles T. Fairbairn of Ishpeming, secretary; W.C. Dewey of Grand Rapids and Frederick Braastad of Ishpeming, directors. The company was capitalized at $2.5 million and leased the Lake Superior 40-acre parcel and the adjacent one to the south.

After the shaft was dewatered, the upper drift was extended 40 feet to the east, striking a rich chimney. The shaft was deepened to 110 feet and the lower drift was extended, following the vein to the west. Three hundred tons of ore were stockpiled, awaiting the purchase of a mill. In March 1890, a test of 50 tons of quartz was made in the Michigan Gold Company's mill. From ore showing no coarse gold, an average of $15.25 per ton in bullion and $5 per ton in concentrate was recovered. The April snow melt flooded the lower levels of the mine, however, and the last mention of the mine in local newspapers indicated that the company planned to strip the vein on the surface. The Gold Lake Mining Company surrendered its lease in 1898, and the mine was never reopened, remaining a potential bonanza to this day.

Many of the early gold mining companies failed long before their properties had been thoroughly explored or developed. The evolution from a promising prospect to a paying mine is an expensive process. Even the Ishpeming Gold Range's most successful mine, the Ropes, eventually failed, in part because the company lacked the money needed to develop the mine for efficient operation.

A strong capital foundation, however, was no guarantee of success, as demonstrated by the fortunes of

Frederick Braastad
Men of Progress

the Superior Gold and Silver Company. Although vigorously backed by such wealthy investors as Marquette banker Peter White, along with promising prospects in three different areas, the company never opened a successful gold mine. Organized in late August 1888, the company leased the NE ¼ of the NE ¼ of Section 35, T48N-R28W, immediately east of the Michigan Gold Company's mine. The quartz vein in which the Michigan Company had found its rich free gold had been traced onto this 40-acre tract, where it was hoped similarly rich deposits would be found. In fact, ore averaging up to $20 per ton was found in a 30-foot shaft on the main vein and on several smaller veins in 1888 and early 1889. Another vein, hoped to be a continuation of the Peninsular formation, was found in the northeast corner of the property. None of these veins, however, proved to be large enough to pay for mining, because they were either too narrow or too inconsistent. In 1890, the Superior Company obtained an option from the Lake Superior Iron Company on the SE ¼ of the NE ¼ of Section 35, T48N-R28W, south of an earlier prospect and cornering on the Michigan Gold Company property. What was believed to be the Michigan vein was stripped and sampled, but this vein, too, failed to give up sought-for riches.

The Superior Gold and Silver Company later explored prospects on the Ropes and Dead River gold ranges, but these ventures also met with failure. The company was organized by Peter White, Edward R. Hall, Clarence R. Ely and Anson B. Miner and it was capitalized at $2.5 million. Peter White, a pioneer businessman from Marquette, was the major stock-

Ishpeming City Directory 1894

holder. Officers included Dr. J.V. Vandeventer as president, C.R. Ely as secretary and A.B. Miner as treasurer. The Superior property was acquired by the Michigan Quartz Silica Company in 1909, and in 1916 the company attempted unsuccessfully to extract gold from Superior ore in its mill at the Michigan mine. Callahan Mining Corporation purchased the Superior along with the Michigan mine in 1985, and it was the site of a program of diamond drilling during 1987 and 1988. Perhaps the new owners believed they would find the rich veins which eluded the Superior company a century ago.

East of the Superior Gold and Silver Company's property on the Michigan range was a prospect worked by the Gitchie Gumie Gold Mining Company. The W ½ of the NW ¼ of Section 36, T48N-R28W, had been explored in 1885 by R.D. Vaughn and his associates. Assays of the quartz vein found there showed enough gold to pay for mining. Vaughn apparently let his option lapse, since the next mention of the property, which was owned by Edward Breitung, a pioneer Negaunee mining man, had the option held by Ephraim Coon. Coon then sold his option to Robert Nelson and Judge Henry H. Mildon in August 1887. A year later, Mildon, along with Coon, W.P. Healy, E.P. Bennett and Nathan M. Kaufman, formed the Gitchie Gumie Gold Mining Company and exercised their option to take a 20-year lease on the northern half of the parcel. Here they erected a blacksmith shop, supply house and a boarding house for the miners. The vein, which was up to six feet wide, was stripped of overburden for 500 feet, and the quartz was mined in the most promising areas. A 40-foot shaft was sunk at one point. Apparently the vein did not prove rich enough to pay, since by July 1889 all work had stopped.

Ishpeming City Directory 1891

57

While George Grummett contested the rights to the rich Michigan vein in the courts, he was also exploring the NE ¼ of the NW ¼ of Section 36, T48N-R28W, one-half mile east of the Michigan mine. Grummett had obtained an option in December 1886 from its owners, Peter and Victoria Gingrass, to explore the forty and leased the parcel a month later. Over the next two years, Grummett opened several test pits and three shafts, the deepest of which eventually reached 62 feet. Some high grade specimens carrying free gold were found, but the vein as a whole did not average rich enough to warrant expansion, and by 1889 the prospect had been abandoned.

After discovering the Lake Superior and Michigan gold veins, A.B. Miner and E.R. Hall continued to explore on the Michigan range. On the SE ¼ of the NW ¼ of Section 36, T48N-R28W, they found a four-foot-wide vein of gold-bearing quartz, apparently a continuation of the Grummett vein. Here they sank a shallow shaft. Late in 1888, they sold the prospect to a group of Chicago and Upper Michigan investors, who formed the Giant Gold and Silver Mining Company. George and Albert Raymond of Chicago had invented a machine to separate gold from its ores and saw the prospect as a way to prove their machine. Along with their partners, George Parmlee of Chicago, H.J. Payne of Escanaba, John McDonald of Iron River and James H. Molloy of Ishpeming, they set six men to work under Captain Richard Trevarthen. No free gold was found in the shaft, although the one assay report made public showed values of $10.40 per ton. The prospect was abandoned in 1889, and the Raymond brothers had to look elsewhere to demonstrate their patented gold separator.

A mile and a half east of the Michigan mine, James and Thomas Dwyer, wholesale liquor dealers from Marquette, found a mineralized quartz vein on their land in 1885. The vein, on the NE ¼ of the NE ¼ of Section 36, T48N-R28W, produced surface samples which assayed up to $11 per ton. Captain William Ward bought a quarter interest in the property and financed further prospecting. A test pit was sunk about five feet into the vein before exploration was halted. Hosea B. Swain, a professional mineral prospector, explored the property for a syndicate of Marquette men in 1888. With his brother, Swain traced the vein for 400 feet on its course across the forty. Several trenches and shallow test pits uncovered gold-bearing quartz assaying up to $121 per ton. However, Swain's backers refused to put up any more money, so he sold his option to Julian M. Case of Marquette.

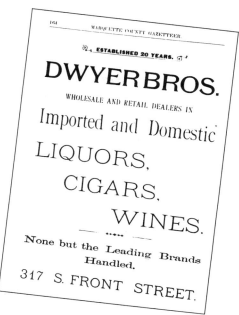

Case bought Ward's interest in the property and immediately set his men to work, sinking a shaft and building a blacksmith shop, supply house and a boarding house for the miners. The shaft followed the vein to a depth of more than 30 feet and produced some finely disseminated free gold. The gold-bearing quartz was mixed with slate, however, and eventually pinched out at depth.

Between the Grummett prospect on the west and the Case on the east was a forty known as the Brown prospect. About 1888, unknown parties found several promising quartz veins and sank some pits and a shallow shaft. The vein was found to be narrow and inconsistent, and work was soon abandoned. It is not known for whom the prospect was named.

One of the most promising gold prospects on the Michigan range was the Peninsular mine. Discovered in 1885 by John Sanson, this prospect was located in a large reef of quartz which ranged up to 50 feet wide. An experienced prospector, Sanson had been exploring west of the Ropes mine for several months on lands owned by Peter Gingrass and the Breitung estate

Marquette County Gazetteer 1889

59

when he discovered gold-bearing quartz in the SW ¼ of the SW ¼ of Section 25, T48N-R28W. He continued to explore the area for two years, selling a less promising prospect to help raise enough capital to purchase an option from Gingrass and to start mining. Working with four men, he ran an adit a short distance into the side of the bluff and sank a shaft 20 feet, finding ore averaging $20 per ton before his money ran out.

Sanson sold the prospect in September 1888 to Alfred Magoon of DePere, Wisconsin, who in turn sold it to a group of Detroit investors who incorporated the Peninsular Gold Mining Company. Principal partners were Francis F. Palms, president; William B. Moran, vice president; Frederick T. Moran, secretary and treasurer; and W.P. Ratigan and Waldo Johnson. William M. Courtis served as mining engineer and consultant. The Peninsular company set a force of men to work under Captain Thomas Trevithic, sinking the shaft to 69 feet, then drifting and crosscutting to test the extent of the vein. The quartz was found to be 31 feet wide at the bottom of the shaft. A drift at the 50-foot level followed the vein 113 feet, while trenching showed it to continue at least 400 feet on the surface, as well as uncovering four other intersecting veins. A second shaft was sunk south of the first, eventually reaching a depth of 80 feet.

Although samples from the shafts and drifts assayed as high as $120 to the ton and specimens were found containing nuggets the size of peas, a mill test was needed to prove what the mine could actually produce. In March 1891, 40 tons of lean ore, with no gold visible, were run through the stamp mills at the Ropes mine, yielding an average of $3 per ton. The

Adit at the Peninsular Gold Mine

Daniel Fountain

60

mine continued to be worked through the summer, proving up the vein, but despite the promising mill test results, the good assays and the abundance of ore available, operations ceased in August 1891. The company had failed to attract enough investors to keep the mine running, and the lease was surrendered to Gingrass the following year.

In 1898, Charles T. Fairbairn and Albert K. Sedgwick, who also held an option on the idled Ropes mine, took an option on the Peninsular property. The shafts were dewatered and samples taken, but not enough gold was found to attract investors to reopen the mine. Another option was taken by parties from the Copper Country in 1901, but apparently no work was done. In 1905, the property was among seven forties taken over by the Ishpeming Gold Mines Company. This company reopened the Michigan as a silica mine but did nothing with the Peninsular.

The property was acquired by Callahan Mining Corporation in 1985. After a program of diamond drilling and surface geological study, Callahan announced in October 1987 that they would reopen the mine. Mining would be carried on by a method similar to that used at the Ropes, with a production level at a depth of 400 feet and two or three mining levels at intervals above that. The ore would be hauled to the surface in underground trucks traveling up an inclined tunnel and would be trucked to Callahan's Humboldt plant for processing. After more than 100 years, it seemed that the Peninsular Mine would finally live up to its promise. Further drilling, however,

AN INVESTOR'S MINE.

DESCRIPTION
OF THE PROPERTY OF

Peninsular Gold Mining Co.

SITUATED ON

THE ISHPEMING RANGE,

IN MICHIGAN.

ITS RESOURCES
AND FUTURE PROMISE.

DETROIT, MICH.:
JOHN F. EBY & CO., PRINTERS,
1889.

Peninsular Prospectus
Daniel Fountain collection

61

did not prove as promising as the earlier work, and the development project was suspended.

In the fall of 1888, attorney J. Maurice Finn of Grayling, Michigan, began exploring for gold near the workings of the Peninsular Gold Company. Tracing the Peninsular vein to the west, he found two promising veins of gold-bearing quartz on the S ½ of the SE ¼ of Section 26, T48N-R28W. Shunning publicity, Finn worked to secure a lease on the two forties from the owners, the heirs of the late Senator Edward N. Breitung of Negaunee. Working as general manager for the newly organized Grayling Gold and Silver Company, he quietly started sinking a shaft on the eastern forty. His secrecy was broken in February 1889 when a local newspaper announced the find, reporting the rock to be so rich that the hand-driven drill used by the prospectors became stuck in the soft native gold. The first blast broke loose more than seven ounces of gold, and some specimens of quartz were found to contain up to $38,000 per ton in gold.

Diamond drill at work at the Peninsular
Daniel Fountain

The company equipped the property with a steam hoist and built a boarding house, nicknamed the "Hotel Breitung," to house the 12 miners. Finn attempted to engage the Peninsular and Michigan companies with the Grayling in the joint purchase of a five stamp mill. Failing in this, the company proposed to buy a 20-ton capacity Huntington centrifugal mill for its own use, but backed out when the manufacturer would not provide a suitable guarantee.

When the shaft reached 60 feet, drifts were started, following the vein to the east and west, and a crosscut to the south sought the other vein which showed on the surface. Specimens rich in native gold were still being found, so the shaft was deepened to 100 feet. In October 1889, the Grayling Company contracted with M.E. Harrington and Son of Ishpeming for a program of diamond drill exploration, the first use of the diamond drill on the Ishpeming Gold Range. The first

drill hole struck the vein at a depth of 400 feet, finding pay rock averaging $28.84 per ton. A second drill hole was started a quarter mile west, near the center of the property, in 1890. A formation of soft rock which caved into the hole slowed the work and eventually stopped the drilling when the diamond bit and drill rod became stuck 250 feet down. Encouraged by the results of the drilling, the company started a shaft at the second drill hole, but ran into trouble sinking through the same soft formation which had stopped the diamond drill. The company quit work shortly thereafter, having spent more than $15,000

Ishpeming City Directory 1891

without any return. The next time the Grayling property was mentioned in the media was in 1894, when it was advertised as being available for exploration at reasonable terms.

In addition to his explorations for the Grayling Gold and Silver Company, Finn had an interest in several other gold prospects. In partnership with Julian M. Case of Marquette, he bought an option on the S ½ of the SW ¼ of Section 26, T48N-R28W, from its owner, Theodore M. Davis. There he found a vein of gold-bearing quartz in the granite country rock. Assays showed $10 per ton, but the vein was too narrow to be worked. Finn also joined with Ishpeming blacksmith Thomas Gaynor to form the Ishpeming Gold and Silver Exploring Company in 1889. They bought an option on the S ½ of the NE ¼ of Section 23, T48N-R28W, where landowner Joseph Pepin had found a 12-inch vein of quartz, but it is not known how much work was done.

J. Maurice Finn left the gold mining business with the closing of the Grayling prospect, but re-entered the public eye when he made an unsuccessful bid for the 12th District Congressional seat in 1892 amid allegations that he had defrauded the state and Nels Mickelson, his former partner in the Grayling Company. Finn left Michigan in 1893, leaving a trail of bad debts behind him. He relocated in Cripple Creek, Colorado, where the Colorado gold rush was in full swing. Finn dabbled in gold mining for a while, but soon resumed the practice of law, adding a collection agency and real estate business. He soon built a fortune buying and selling gold properties and handling miners' legal disputes. When vice-presidential nominee Teddy Roosevelt visited Cripple Creek during the campaign of 1900, Finn invited him to be his guest the next time he visited the West. Roosevelt accepted, so Finn proceeded to build a palatial mansion in the best section of town. This grand home, known to the locals as "Finn's Folly," was five stories high and boasted an observatory and an indoor trout pond surrounding its central stairway. Vice-President Roosevelt visited Finn in the spring of 1901, proclaiming "Finn's Folly"

64

to be the most beautiful home in Colorado.

The NW ¼ of the SE ¼ of Section 35, T48N-R28W, south of the Michigan mine, was explored by George Cummings in 1888 with unknown results. Cummings was married to Hannah Ropes, the sister of Julius Ropes, and was a partner in the Ropes Gold and Silver Company. He was a highly respected mineral explorer and had discovered the Holyoke Silver Mine in 1864, but he was a very secretive man. One of his last acts before he died was to burn his life's collection of geological notes, perhaps destroying information on mineral deposits undiscovered to this day.

Late in 1888, Ishpeming merchants Richard and John Mockler found a 3 ½-foot vein of gold-bearing quartz a mile southwest of the Michigan mine on the SW ¼ of the SW ¼ of Section 35, T48N-R28W. The brothers sank an exploratory shaft to a depth of 25 feet and found

GEO. P. CUMMINGS,
—— LAND AGENT,——
EXPLORER and CIVIL ENGINEER
LANDS BOUGHT AND SOLD.
Explorations for Minerals, Timber, etc., made, Taxes Paid, Trespass Prevented, Titles Examined and Adjusted, Lands Located at State and Government Offices. Minutes of Pine and Mineral Lands for Sale.
MARQUETTE, L. S., - - MICHIGAN.

free gold assaying up to $17.50 per ton, but not in enough quantity to make the prospect pay. Explorations were limited to the fall and winter of 1888.

Three quarters of a mile west of the Mockler shaft

George Cummings
Biographical Record

Michigan State Gazetteer 1881

are two shafts and a number of trenches, the explorations of two other early mining companies. Organized in July 1888, the Lake Superior Gold Mining Compa-

ny leased the E ½ of the SW ¼ of Section 34, T48N-R28W, where a vein of gold-bearing quartz had been found, from the East Saginaw Iron Company. The company's founders, Richard Blake, Irving D. Hanscom and C.F. Conrad of Marquette, offered stock for sale at 10 cents per share to finance exploration. The

Ishpeming City Directory 1891

company explored by trenching and test pitting and sank a shaft at least 38 feet before giving up the pros-

Michigan State Gazetteer 1891-2

pect. A year later, a company of Detroit capitalists

66

formed the Detroit Gold Mining Company. Dr. H.O. Walker was president, and L.H. Collins served as secretary. The company was reported to hold a very promising forty on Section 34, but it is not known

RICHARD BLAKE,
DEALER IN
Real Estate and Pine.
TIMBER AND MINERAL LANDS.
City Business and Residence Property for Sale. Sole Agent for the Longyear
Addition to Marquette.
HARLOW BLOCK.

if they took over the Lake Superior Company's workings or opened a new prospect of their own.

Although the Michigan Gold Range ran generally east and west through Sections 35 and 36, promising quartz veins were also found on several sections to the north. The Peninsular, Grayling and Finn-Case prospects were located immediately north on Sections 25 and 26. Section 23, T48N-R28W, owned by Leon Pepin, was also the site of several explorations in 1887 and 1888, including the previously mentioned Ishpeming Gold and Silver Exploring Company, which was located in the NW ¼ of the section.

In 1888, Dr. A.E. Gourdeau, the county physician, took an option on the SE ¼ of the SW ¼ of Section 23 and set a few men to work exploring. On the adjacent forty to the west, a Hungarian immigrant named Smith was sinking a shaft into an outcropping of quartz. The shaft reached a depth of 22 feet before Smith sold out. A group of Ishpeming men, led by Frederick Braastad, the owner of the Winthrop Iron Mine, and Moses B. Toutloff, proprietor of the Hotel Toutloff, purchased the Gourdeau and Smith options and began exploring in the spring of 1889. The local men attracted the attention of investors from Grand

Marquette City Directory 1891

67

Rapids and formed the Grand Rapids and Ishpeming Gold and Silver Company. Braastad served as president, Toutloff was treasurer, T. Hughes was the secretary and C.L. Love served as business agent. Smith's shaft was pumped out, and testing of the vein was resumed. Aside from one newspaper article reporting that "fine quartz" was being found, the prospect was never mentioned in the media again.

*Ishpeming City
Directory 1886-7*

*Marquette County
Gazetteer, 1889*

CHAPTER FOUR

Ropes Range Prospects

L ocated on the western 40 acres adjacent to the Ropes mine, the Phillips Gold Mine was a typical prospect on the Ishpeming Gold Range in that it never produced any appreciable amount of gold. The Phillips was unusual, however, because it may have been an outright fraud.

The land surrounding the Ropes Gold Mine was owned by the Deer Lake Iron Company, mainly as a source of hardwood to make into charcoal for the Deer Lake blast furnace. After mining at the Ropes in 1883 began to prove the vein's value, the Deer Lake Company, under its manager William H. Rood, began exploring for gold on its lands to the east and west of the Ropes along the strike of the vein. Early in 1884, a vein of gold-bearing quartz five feet wide was found about a quarter mile west of the Ropes shaft on the SE ¼ of the NE ¼ of Section 30, T48N-R27W. An 8-by-10-foot test shaft was sunk upon it. The miners were still finding rich quartz when water seeping into the shaft stopped the sinking at 40 feet.

Later in 1884, the Phillips Gold Mining Company was formed to purchase and mine the vein on the Deer Lake Company's land. Incorporated in Springfield, Illinois, under the laws of that state, the company was founded by portrait painter John Phillips, iron ore capitalist H.R. Dunkee, real estate tycoon Andrew J. Cooper, Roswell B. Bacon and W.H.A. Brown, all of Chicago, and Joseph Sellwood of Ishpeming. The company purchased the property for $40,000,

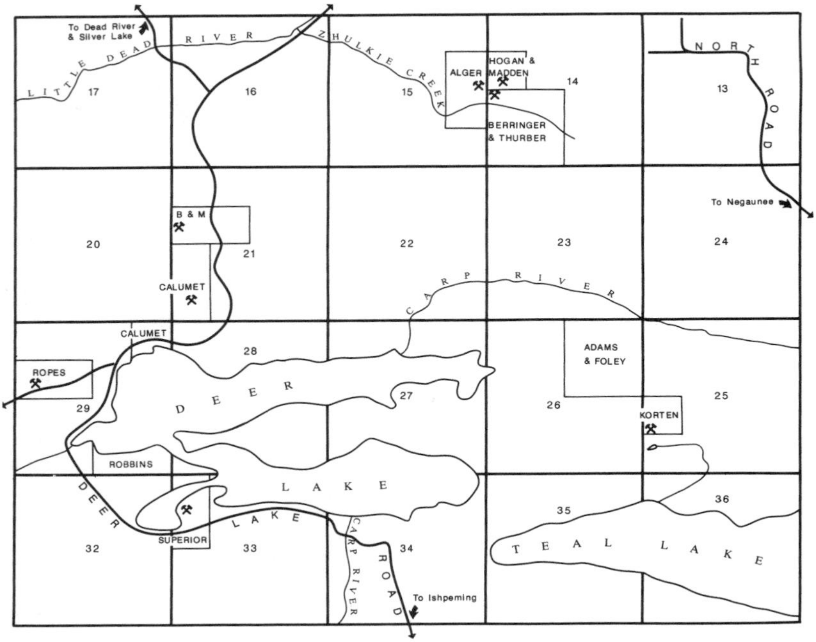

offering 100,000 shares of stock at $10 apiece, a price local newspapers considered unreasonably high for an unproven prospect.

Under Superintendent John Davies, an experienced gold miner from Colorado and one of the company's strongest promoters, the miners dewatered the existing shaft excavated by the Deer Lake Company using the boiler and steam engine from the original Ropes stamp mill. The Phillips company also decided to drive an adit into the side of the hill some 50 feet east of the existing shaft. When this tunnel reached the nearly vertical quartz vein 35 feet into the hill, a second shaft was sunk, following the vein and intersecting the adit. Assays of samples from the surface of the vein showed $5 to $12 in gold, and at 22 feet in the new shaft the quartz was said to average $36 per ton. The company announced plans to sink the shaft to 150 feet and install a stamp mill to extract the gold, but by 60 feet the vein had either pinched out or angled away from the shaft. The company continued to sink the shaft, searching for a continuation

The Ropes Gold Range
NMU Cartographic Lab

of the vein, and eventually reached a depth of 90 feet in late-1885.

While the prospect was producing rich gold samples, Superintendent Davies and Charles Ralston, the local agent for the Phillips company, promoted the stock heavily, both in the local area and in the Chicago and Milwaukee markets. Ambitious plans to build a 25 stamp mill were announced in 1885. When the shaft lost the vein, however, the company withdrew its stock from sale in the local area, and Davies and Ralston were little to be seen. In the downstate markets, the stock continued to be sold at about the same price as Ropes Gold and Silver Company stock.

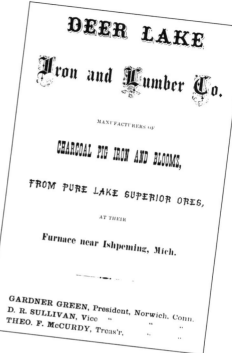

DEER LAKE

Iron and Lumber Co.

MANUFACTURERS OF

CHARCOAL PIG IRON AND BLOOMS,

FROM PURE LAKE SUPERIOR ORES,

AT THEIR

Furnace near Ishpeming, Mich.

GARDNER GREEN, President, Norwich. Conn.
D. R. SULLIVAN, Vice   "   "
THEO. F. McCURDY, Treas'r, ...

By March 1886, all work had been abandoned and the company's representatives had disappeared from the area. Taxes on the property were left unpaid after 1888, and the land and mineral rights eventually reverted to the state. Callahan Mining Corporation bought the property in 1983, but no plans to reopen the prospect have been announced. Although the mine may have been a legitimate prospect in the beginning, it seems the objective of the Phillips Gold Mining Company was to mine gold from investors' pockets, rather than from veins of quartz.

By the spring of 1889, the Superior Gold and Silver Company had nearly given up on its property adjacent to the Michigan mine. About that time, Julius Ropes found a new gold vein on Section 33, T48N-R27W, just south of the Carp River between the Ropes mine and the Deer Lake Furnace. Ropes and *Beard's Directory of Marquette County 1873* his associates had enough faith in their new prospect to announce plans to install a stamp mill as soon as possible. This inspired the Superior Gold and Silver Company to buy the prospect, comprising the W ½ of the NW ¼ of the section, financed by a 10-cent-per-share assessment. The prospect on the Michigan vein was abandoned, the blacksmith shop and mining equipment were moved to the new prospect and by mid-June a 15-foot shaft had been sunk on the vein. Again, despite vigorous exploration and assays showing up to $179 per ton, economic quantities of gold were not to be found.

Early in 1883, Captain George Berringer, an experienced iron mining man, found a six-foot-wide vein two miles northeast of the Ropes on the SW ¼ of Section 14, T48N-R27W, near Zhulkie Creek. Here he sank one test shaft on top of a hill and a second one farther east in a hollow. Encouraged by assays showing up to $30 per ton in gold and silver, and financed by prominent lumberman Henry C. Thurber of Marquette, he continued sinking the shaft to 50 feet, sending the rock to smelters in Chicago and Newark

DEER LAKE FURNACE AND FALLS.

The Deer Lake Furnace

Iron Ore

for testing. Lack of capital forced the mine to be shut down during the winter. The mine reopened in July 1884 with financial backing from a pool of Chicago investors, who confidently made plans to erect a stamp mill. Further work, including sinking the shaft

72

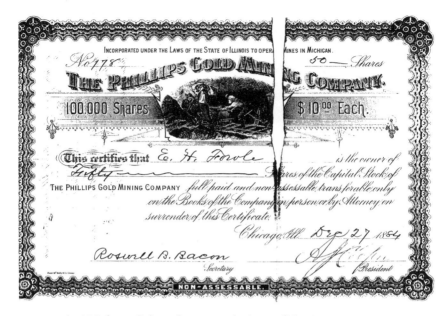

INCORPORATED UNDER THE LAWS OF THE STATE OF ILLINOIS TO OPER... ...INES IN MICHIGAN.

No. 478

THE PHILLIPS GOLD MINING COMPANY.

50 — Shares

100,000 Shares — $10.00 Each.

This certifies that E. H. Fowle is the owner of Fifty — Shares of the Capital Stock of THE PHILLIPS GOLD MINING COMPANY full paid and non-assessable, transferable only on the Books of the Company in person or by Attorney on surrender of this Certificate.

Chicago, Ill. Dec 27 1884

Roswell B. Bacon
Secretary

President

NON-ASSESSABLE.

to nearly 100 feet, did not bear out their confidence, and by December the prospect was closed for good.

West of the Berringer & Thurber prospect, and apparently on the same vein, a group of Negaunee men started a small shaft late in the summer of 1883. Organizing the Negaunee Gold and Silver Company, they leased the SE ¼ of the NE ¼ and the NE ¼ of the SE ¼ of Section 15, T48N-R27W. The miners sank the shaft to 41 feet and found ore worth up to $50 per ton before ceasing work that fall. The prospect sat idle until the next fall, when the company was reorganized as the Alger Gold Mining Company, named in honor of Michigan's Civil War hero (and later governor) Russell A. Alger. Rock assaying up to $34.90 per ton was found, with nearly half the value in silver. The shaft was worked for about a month, reaching a depth of 60 feet by the end of December. The vein proved inconsistent, however, and work was stopped again until spring. In April, work was resumed, and by the end of August 1885 the shaft was 90 feet deep. Thirty-dollar ore was still being found,

Phillips stock certificate
Negaunee Historical Society

73

John Q. Adams
Daniel Fountain collection

but not in sufficient quantity to pay, so the prospect was abandoned. Among the principals in the Negaunee and Alger companies were Messrs. Morse, Dougherty, Davis, J.F. Stevens, Thomas M. Wells, attorney John Q. Adams, Negaunee *Iron Herald* publisher Clinton G. Griffey, Joseph M. Gannon, iron mining superintendent James F. Foley, Edward Blake and Mathias Schweisenthal.

In the fall of 1883, a third prospect was opened on the Berringer vein. Negaunee businessmen Phillip Madden, a saloon keeper, and Phillip Hogan, who sold "temperance drinks," along with Peter Fitzpatrick and John T. Hayes, started a small shaft on the SW ¼ of the NW ¼ of Section 14, T48N-R27W. In October, they released assay reports showing up to $4.13 in gold and $21.34 in silver per ton. The shaft was sunk about 20 feet before being shut down for the winter. Work was resumed the next August, and the shaft was sunk another 10 feet, with unknown results. No further assays were made public, but Hogan, Madden and Fitzpatrick organized a stock company along with Messrs. Mooney, Molloy and Welsh of Ishpeming. The company announced plans to sink a second shaft 200 feet south of the first and carry it down at least 100 feet, but this was the last mention of the prospect in the local media.

The Teal Lake Gold and Silver Exploring Company prospected on Section 25, T48N-R27W, and adjacent sections north of Teal Lake in 1885. The company worked under a three-month option from the Michigan Land and Iron Company, but did not announce any find of precious metals. Officers in the company were A.A. Anderson, president; W.O. Tislov, treasurer; and C.W. McMahon, secretary.

In the spring of 1889, the Korten Gold and Silver Company was formed in Negaunee to explore lands north of Teal Lake, where George Korten had discovered quartz carrying free gold. Peter E. Gingrass and John W. Jochim of Ishpeming were elected president and treasurer, respectively, and Christopher Roessler

and city attorney James L. McLear of Negaunee were vice president and secretary. The company traced the vein across the NW ¼ of the SW ¼ of Section 25, T48N-R27W, and reported finding specimens carrying gold and silver worth up to $35 per ton. During

Michigan State Gazetteer 1885

Michigan State Gazetteer 1887-8

75

the summer of 1890, after a change of management, the company stoped into the bluff and sank a shaft at the richest spot on the vein, but failed to find pay rock.

Negaunee experienced another period of gold fever in 1891, when Abram Boulsom found a mineralized vein on Section 23, T48N-R27W, about three miles northwest of town. Boulsom was a merchant tailor who owned a shop on Iron Street and served as alderman from the city's second ward. Boulsom and several associates formed the Boulsom Gold Mining Company (which was later reorganized as the Negaunee Gold and Silver Mining Company) and sank a shaft 80 feet into the vein, which was up to nine feet wide. Assays of specimens from the shaft showed up to $182 in gold, and as much as 80 ounces of silver per ton. Over the next three months at least two other discoveries were made in the vicinity of the Boulsom shaft. Apparently none of these prospects panned out. Three years later, however, James Morgan, who had been in charge of the Negaunee Gold and Silver Mining Company's explorations, took an option on the property. Although he reopened the shaft and deepened it, no more gold was found.

As the gold boom died down in the 1890s, few prospectors continued to search the countryside for gold. Only the Ropes mine continued to produce the yellow metal, and even it was running on a shoestring. The promising country between the Ropes and Michigan mines had been explored, and although a number of pits and shafts had been opened, no bonanzas

Ishpeming City Directory 1891

76

were found. Only a few dedicated prospectors continued to search for riches.

Ishpeming clothing merchant and mineral explorer Edward Robbins was one such prospector. He had explored for minerals in the iron and gold ranges for years. In 1887, he found a small gold-bearing vein, assaying $7.56 per ton, on the S ½ of the SE ¼ of Section 29, T48N-R27W, near what is now known as Gold Mine Creek. Along with tailor George H. Arthur, he explored the E ½ of the SE ¼ of Section 31, T48N-R27W, about a mile southwest, reportedly with promising results. During the fall and winter of 1888, Robbins and Arthur traced the vein, which was two to four feet wide, some 500 feet on the surface and reported favorable assays. The next spring, they reported

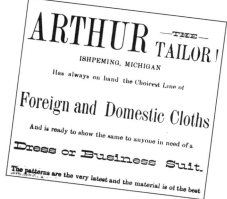

finding a three-foot vein of quartz carrying pyrite and chalcopyrite three miles east on Section 34, T48N-R27W. None of these prospects held enough gold to pay, however.

In 1894, Robbins turned his attention to Section 21, T48N-R27W, midway between the Ropes mine and

Michigan State Gazetteer 1887-8

Iron Ore

the Berringer and Thurber vein. A three-foot vein of quartz, bearing silver and gold, had been found in this area by R.D. Vaughn, Robert Maxwell and Charles H. Kirkwood in 1885, but little other exploration had been done. Within a few hundred yards of the charcoal-making location of Ten Kilns and the county highway leading north to the old Coon and Fire Centre prospects, Robbins found a vein of quartz carrying pyrite, chalcopyrite, hematite and up to $610 per ton in gold. He leased the land from its owner, the Michigan Land and Iron Company, subject to a 10-percent royalty on any precious minerals produced. Although the vein continued to yield rich specimens, Robbins continued to search during 1894 and 1895 for larger veins and found an extension of the vein 2,000 feet to the west. He died in 1896 without opening a shaft to prove up his discovery.

Two years later, James H. Billings and William Murdoch secured a lease on the S ½ of the NW ¼ of Section 21, where Robbins had made his richest finds. Murdoch, the proprietor of the Murdoch House, was a retired clown known as ''Uncle Billy'' who had

Ishpeming City Directory 1886-7

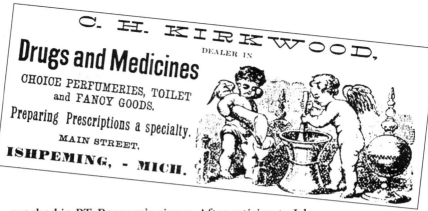

worked in P.T. Barnum's circus. After retiring to Ish-peming, he continued to entertain the local children on special occasions. Along with Judge Henry H. Mildon and Anson B. Miner, Billings and Murdoch formed the B&M Gold Company. Frederick H. Begole was elected president, with Billings as vice-president and Randall P. Bronson as secretary/treasurer. The company, financed by its incorporators, started sink-ing a shaft, following the vein to 20 feet by March 1898. By the time the shaft reached 50 feet, howev-er, the vein had narrowed. The company drifted some 37 feet, optimistically expecting to strike "some pretty good looking quartz" when they hit the "main vein." The main vein was never found, and the company ceased operations late in 1898.

In 1935, Elmer Strathman leased the B&M property from the Ford Motor Company, which had bought out the land holdings of the Michigan Land and Iron Company. Inspired by the reopening of the Ropes and Michigan mines, as well as the increase in the price of gold to $35 an ounce, he started a one-man min-ing operation at the old shaft. He built a grinding mill from a steel drum and water pipe and set up a hoist powered by a Model T Ford on the waste rock pile in front of the hillside shaft. Strathman apparently had no better luck finding the main vein than the B&M company had.

A pair of small shafts located half a mile south of the B&M shaft are the only remaining traces of the

Michigan State Gazetteer 1885

Calumet Gold and Silver Mining Company. In the fall of 1883, the Calumet company took an option on the NW ¼ of the NW ¼ of Section 29, T48N-R27W, just north of the Ropes. The prospect was disappointing, however, so the company turned its attention to the W ½ of the SW ¼ of Section 21, T48N-R27W, which it also held under option. The miners worked into the winter sinking two shafts 100 feet apart, but failed to find pay rock. The Calumet Gold and Silver Mining Company was founded by John Quincy Adams of Negaunee, president, Joseph Sellwood of Ishpeming, vice president, Joseph C. Foley of Chicago, secretary/treasurer, and James F. Foley of Negaunee and D. Kloeckner of Hancock, directors.

During the summer of 1894, James Ames and Peter J. Lundquist of Ishpeming, who had discovered the Ames Iron Mine east of Ishpeming the previous year, began prospecting for gold. After unsuccessfully exploring a forty adjacent to the Peninsular mine, they moved their operation to Section 31, T48N-R27W, near Edward Robbins' earlier find. When they discovered a six-inch vein of gold-bearing quartz, they leased the south half of the section from the Cleveland Cliffs Iron Company and sank a shaft. Ames and Lundquist mined several tons of ore and reported assays of up to $50 per ton, but did not find enough rich ore to make the prospect pay.

On Section 18, T48N-R27W, some two miles north of the Ropes mine, Anson B. Miner, one of the discoverers of the Michigan mine, was reported to have found gold. Located in 1885, the well-defined vein produced some good specimens. Details of the location and value of the vein are lacking.

The Anglo-American Land and Mineral Company was formed in 1885 by W.A. Allen, R.H. Taylor and Byron Jones of Negaunee. The company was organized to develop gold and silver properties in the Marquette County area, but the location of the company's lands is unknown.

Richard Crow, a highly experienced mining man from Boulder City, Colorado, was the mill superintendent at the Ropes mine. Recognizing the possibili-

ty of further gold veins being found nearby, he joined
with Anson Miner and Joseph Sellwood, the general
manager of the Ropes mine, in exploring to the east
on Section 27, T48N-R27W. Crow sank a 10-foot
shaft into a small vein late in 1884 and produced a
small amount of rock worth from $5 to $18 per ton.

About the same time, James F. Foley and John Quincy Adams of Negaunee, partners in the Hematite Mining Company, found gold-bearing rock two miles east
of the Ropes mine. Located on the NE ¼ of Section
26, T48N-R27W, the prospect yielded specimens carrying up to $34 in gold and silver, but was abandoned
by 1885.

Twelve years later, in 1896, Charles T. Fairbairn, William Brooks and J.O. Flack resumed explorations on
the same section. The men found a vein up to 10 feet
wide and several hundred feet long, but assays of rock
from their 16-foot shaft proved disappointing. Fairbairn continued to explore the area, however, and in
1900 found a small vein of quartz carrying as much
as $48 in gold to the ton, but no mining was done.

In 1936, a group of investors, including Houghton
attorneys Allen F. Rees and Dean Robinson, incor-

Elmer Strathman
with his Model T-
powered hoist at
the B&M Gold
Mine
Superior View Studio

81

porated the Norgan Gold Mining Company. The company conducted extensive explorations across the gold ranges on lands optioned from the Ford Motor Company, which had bought up the holdings of the Michigan Land and Iron Company. Late in 1936, Norgan's prospectors found a vein of quartz carrying chalcopyrite on the SW ¼ of the NW ¼ of Section 30, T48N-R26W, north of Teal Lake near the Carp River. Samples from the three-foot-wide vein assayed up to 0.6 ounces per ton in gold ($21 at the new price of $35 per ton). The following year, the company sank two shallow shafts on the vein, but apparently failed to find paying quantities of gold.

CHAPTER FIVE

The Dead River Gold Range

D uring the 1860s, the area near Silver Lake and along the Dead River was the scene of a silver exploration boom. In the summer of 1863, a Native American who had acquired some knowledge of minerals while working with pioneer iron ore prospectors showed Silas C. Smith a vein of silver-bearing lead ore about 15 miles northwest of Ishpeming. The "Smith Vein," as it became known, was located on Section 6, T49N-R28W, near Silver Lake. This vein became the Lake Superior Silver Lead Mine and started a "silver rush" in which thousands of acres of land were bought and sold, and at least 35 mining companies were incorporated. The Marquette County Board of Supervisors felt that the finds were valuable enough that they appropriated $6,000 to finance a road from Marquette to the Silver Lake district.

Most of the silver mining companies never opened mines on their land. Many of the claims were on barren ground, having been bought during the winter of 1863-64, when five feet of snow hid any possible indications of mineral veins. One mine which was developed, however, was the Holyoke Silver Mine. Discovered in May 1864, by George P. Cummings and R.S. Livermore, the Holyoke was situated on Section 2, T48N-R28W. Over the next few years, four shafts were sunk and an adit was driven 636 feet in an attempt to strike the vein. No silver production was ever recorded, and the mine was closed in 1868.

In 1890, Julius Ropes, who had discovered the Ish-

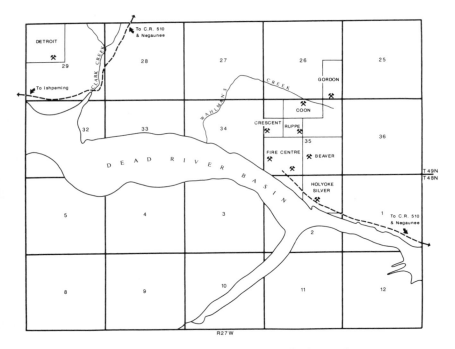

peming Gold Range, identified another, separate range of gold-bearing mineral deposits. Stretching from near Lake Superior to Silver Lake, the newly identified range was described by Ropes as consisting of knobs and ridges of granite, diorite and greenstone laced with quartz veins carrying free gold along with silver, pyrite, copper ore, galena, zinc ore and the only reported occurrence of tellurium in Michigan.

Ropes' findings were hardly the first discovery of gold in the Dead River region, however. During the silver-lead boom of 1864, prospectors exploring for silver on the NE ¼ of the NE ¼ of Section 10, T49N-R28W, near the Rocking Chair Lakes, found a quartz vein carrying pyrite and galena. The Marquette Silver Mining Company, which owned the land, sent samples of the rock to Philadelphia for assay. Professor A. DuBois and Charles P. Williams, the analytic chemists who performed the assay, reported that "the value of the ton of rock is above the average of that of Colorado." Later assays showed as much as $241 in gold per ton of ore. The company trenched and

The Dead River
Gold Range
NMU Cartographic Lab

sank a shallow shaft on the vein but never found economic quantities of either gold or silver. Assays of specimens from other prospects on the silver-lead range showed up to $130 per ton in gold. Some of the silver mining companies, such as the American Gold and Silver Lead Mining Company, the Cincinnati Gold and Silver Mining Company and the Union Gold Company, optimistically included "gold" in their titles and advertising, but none of them ever opened a gold mine.

Some eight miles southeast of the Marquette Silver Mining Company's prospect, Charles Ruppe, along with Joseph Loranger and M. Carey, found a vein of quartz carrying gold and copper ore in 1884. Ruppe's prospect was in the NW ¼ of Section 35, T49N-R27W (the same quarter section where Ropes later opened the Crescent prospect). Over the next three years, Ruppe sank two shafts and reported finding ore worth up to $30 per ton. Located near the head of a long valley, the shafts were 10 and 32 feet deep.

Nearly half a mile to the north, at the foot of the valley, Ephraim Coon of Ishpeming found an extension of the Ruppe vein in 1884. Coon optioned the NE ¼ of the NW ¼ and the NW ¼ of the NE ¼ of Section 35, T49N-R27W, and started work. Shaft sinking and testing revealed ore containing 25 to 50 per cent copper, as well as gold worth up to $39

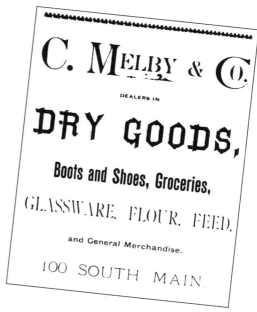

C. MELBY & CO.

DEALERS IN

DRY GOODS,

Boots and Shoes, Groceries,

GLASSWARE, FLOUR, FEED,

and General Merchandise.

100 SOUTH MAIN.

per ton. In July 1885, the Coon Gold Mining Company was incorporated. Ishpeming's mayor, Christian Melby, was elected president, with Montgomery

Ishpeming City Directory 1886-7

Thompson as vice-president and Cornelius Kennedy as treasurer.

The company cut a wagon road to the mine from the Ten Kilns location north of Ishpeming and spent the summer prospecting for additional veins. Further shaft sinking was hampered by water entering the shaft, which was located at the bottom of a valley, only a few feet away from a seasonal stream which would grow from a trickle to a raging torrent after every storm. With financial help from Copper Country investors, a boiler and steam pump were purchased and hauled to the mine in March 1886, and mining was resumed. With the spring snow melt, however, the shaft, which had reached a depth of 40 feet, was flooded again. The steam pump proved inadequate to keep the water down, and the prospect was abandoned. Today, no sign remains of the shaft except the rock dump and the iron pipe from the steam pump. The shaft itself has been completely filled by sediment washed down the valley.

North of the Ruppe and Coon prospects on the Dead River Range was a prospect started in September 1885 by a group of men from the Copper Country. Headed by lumberman John R. Gordon, they explored across a wide valley from the Coon on Section 26, T49N-R27W. On the E ½ of the SE ¼ of the section, they found a gold- and silver-bearing vein, which *Iron Ore* they explored from an adit into the side of the hill.

By the end of October, the adit was 35 feet into the eight-foot-wide vein. An assay showed $8.56 per ton in gold and silver. At a meeting in January 1886, the investors decided that the prospect was rich enough to warrant further exploration and ordered that a shaft should be sunk on the vein. The gold-bearing quartz was reported to have increased in width and richness as the depth increased, and in March, Gordon announced plans to expand operations. Arrangements were made to build a new camp, hire more men and equip the prospect with a boiler, air compressor and power drills. A contract was let to sink the shaft another 50 feet. Gordon met later that month with investors from Chicago, hoping to interest them in the mine, but apparently had no luck. Work was abandoned some time later, the gold ore (and perhaps the working capital) having proven too scarce.

In 1888, John Sanson, the discoverer of the Peninsular Mine, prospected north of the Dead River between Silver Lake and the old Holyoke Silver Mine. Near the northeast corner of Section 25, T49N-

Shaft at the Holyoke Silver Mine, circa 1864
Marquette County Historical Society

87

R28W, he found a four-foot quartz vein carrying galena with silver and gold. Sanson obtained an option on the E ½ of the NE ¼ of the section from its owner, the Michigan Land and Iron Company. He soon sold his option to John McDonald of Iron River who, along with investors from Ishpeming, Chicago and Oconto, Wisconsin, incorporated the Dead River Gold Mining Company. McDonald sold his option to

the company for 13 percent of the new company's stock and became one of the directors. Other major stockholders were Henry W. Walker of Chicago, William B. and Sarah F. High of Oconto, and James H. Molloy of Ishpeming. The company set two shifts of men to work, and eventually sank three or four shallow shafts. By the fall of 1889, McDonald was showing off specimens of gold-bearing quartz and claiming that he had the richest gold mine on earth. However, this "richest gold mine" was never again men-

Adit at the
Gordon prospect
Daniel Fountain

tioned in the press, so it may be assumed that no more pay rock was found.

By the fall of 1890, John McDonald was promoting another gold prospect a mile and a half to the east. He was able to interest investors from Lower Michigan and Wisconsin, and, in October 1890, organized the Detroit Gold and Silver Mining Company. J. VanKirk of Janesville, Wisconsin, was elected president, with Frederick F. Campau of Detroit as vice president and Alex Richardson of Janesville as secretary. McDonald and Edward Campau served as directors.

The new company leased the NW ¼ of Section 29, T49N-R27W, from the Michigan Land and Iron Company, and started driving an adit into the southern point of a hill, just above the level of the plain. By October 1890, the adit was 15 feet into the hill on an 18-foot vein of gold-bearing quartz. Assays of the vein rock ranged from $2.48 to $428.28 per ton, and the adit was continued 50 feet into the hillside. The vein was exposed at four other points on the property and a small shaft was started at the richest showing, up a small valley to the northwest of the adit. The shaft reached an undetermined depth before the prospect closed down.

Years later, the Detroit adit served quite a different purpose. During Prohibition, some enterprising Ish-

Ishpeming City Directory 1891

89

peming men found the isolated mine tunnel to be an excellent location for a moonshine still. The men would haul the ingredients in on their backs several miles from the nearest road. Remnants of their "cooker" can still be found at the site.

In 1890, Charles Ruppe and Charles Kobi of Ishpeming, along with George Weatherston of the Ropes mine, obtained a mining option on the S ½ of the NW ¼ of Section 35, T49N-R27W. Ruppe and Kobi soon sold their interest in the option to the Superior Gold and Silver Company, which had two unsuccessful prospects on the Michigan and Ropes gold ranges, for 1,500 shares of the company's stock. The Superior Company sank several test pits and a shallow shaft, but their luck was no better here, and little gold was found. The prospect was apparently shut down the same year.

Detroit Gold and Silver Company's adit *Daniel Fountain*

During the summer of 1891, Julius Ropes explored lands in the Dead River area which were held under

90

option by the Dead River Miners' Pool. The land was owned by the Michigan Land and Iron Company, which was to collect a 10 percent royalty on any minerals produced. This was later reduced to a more reasonable five percent. Ropes' most promising find was on the SE ¼ of Section 35, T49N-R27W, where he found a three-foot vein of quartz carrying galena and pyrite along with silver and gold assaying up to $502 per ton. This prospect was named the Beaver exploration for the beaver dams on a nearby creek. Two shifts of miners worked to sink a shaft to a depth of 18 feet before a forest fire on July 11, 1891, destroyed their camp and forced the men to take to the Dead River to avoid the heat and flames. During the next two months the log camp was rebuilt and the shaft was sunk to 50 feet, at which depth drifts were started to the east and west.

In August 1891, members of the exploring pool, including Solomon S. Curry of Ishpeming and Charles F. Pfister, Hyatt S. Haselton and George A. Masser of Milwaukee, incorporated the Fire Centre Mining Company, naming it for the igneous origin of the rock of the Dead River Range. Curry was elected president and Haselton served as secretary. The company continued work at the Beaver shaft and started a second shaft just over the hill to the south at a point where quartz holding free gold was found. This became known as the South Beaver lode. Ropes, in his capacity as chief prospector for the Fire Centre Company, also located a new vein half a mile to the west. Located just south of Silver Mine Lake, the new find was named the Crescent prospect. This vein, on the side of a hogsback hill, was worked as an open cut rather than by sinking a shaft. An adit was driven into the side of the hill to search for additional veins.

In 1892, 254 tons of ore from the Fire Centre prospects were hauled by wagon to the Ropes Gold Mine and treated in the stamp mill. The ore proved to be easily stamped and of good grade, producing $2,063.69 in bullion, an average of $8.12 per ton. This successful mill test encouraged the company to continue to develop the mine and to install a small Crawford mill

capable of milling 10 tons per day. When the mill was started up that fall, however, it was found to be unsuitable for the hard ore, wearing out completely within a month. Representatives from the manufacturer repaired the mill early in 1893, shortly before the mine closed for the winter. By this time, the South Beaver shaft had reached a depth of more than 120 feet. The North Beaver shaft was at least 50 feet deep and had more than 100 feet of drifts.

Although the Fire Centre Company announced its intention to resume operations the next spring, the mine was never worked again, the vein apparently having pinched out at depth. The mill machinery was taken to the Ropes mine where the Crawford mill was given another test run in July 1893, again proving a total failure.

The Dead River Range was still considered a promising area, and prospectors continued to seek gold and silver in the hills north of the river. The Fire Centre property was optioned in 1903 by unidentified parties, but no mining was done. In 1914, the property was optioned by John Doelle of Houghton, but again nothing was done beyond exploration. During the summer of 1936, the Norgan Gold Mining Company set crews to exploring Section 35, T49N-R27W, starting with surface trenching. That fall, the company rafted a diamond drill across the Dead River basin and drilled 13 holes totaling 2,000 feet. A few rich areas were found, but the veins were not persistent and the property was abandoned.

CHAPTER SIX

Other Marquette County Prospects

T he most significant gold finds in Marquette County were clustered in a few areas near Ishpeming, but gold veins have also been found in other scattered areas around the county.

The rugged hills near the Morgan blast furnace east of Negaunee attracted a number of prospectors over the years. Silas C. Smith, a pioneer prospector, found a vein of silver-lead at an undisclosed site in this area in the mid-1860s. The vein was reported to run $70 per ton in silver, but Smith was unable to obtain a lease from the owner of the land, the Iron Cliffs Company, so the prospect was abandoned. Some 20 years later, the aged Smith enlisted the help of Peter White to persuade the iron company to grant them a lease. White succeeded, but Smith died before he was able to relocate the site. White hired James E. Jopling of Ishpeming to head a crew of explorers in prospecting the area. Jopling found a 10-foot vein containing lead ore near Bruce, a stop on the Duluth, South Shore and Atlantic Railroad (near Bagdad Pond on the present Wisconsin Central Railroad). Assays of the vein rock revealed only a trace of silver, however, and the prospect was again abandoned.

With the gold excitement stirred up by the production at the Ropes Gold Mine in Ishpeming in the early 1880s, prospectors searched the Morgan area for gold veins. Late in 1884, Negaunee Justice of the Peace John Jones, butcher Charles Muck and merchant Gottlieb Sporley discovered a vein of rich copper ore not far from Morgan. The vein was reported to range from 14 inches to six feet in width. Assays showed as much as 43 percent copper, along with $3 to $19.38 per ton in gold, and from a trace to $21 in silver per ton of ore. Through the summer of 1885, three men worked at sinking a shaft into the vein, eventually reaching a depth of 18 feet. The partners apparently sold their prospect to state Senator Edward Breitung that fall, when a local paper noted that "Hon. Edward Breitung has a prospect near Morgan which may turn out to be anything from a copper mine to a gold mine." It seems that it became neither, since no further mention of the prospect was made in the media. A shallow shaft sunk on a quartz vein in the SW ¼ of the SW ¼ of Section 25, T48N-R26W, a few hundred yards northwest of the old Morgan Heights Sanatorium may belong to this prospect.

When the Lake Superior and Ishpeming Railroad was built in 1896, it was routed parallel to the DSS&A Railroad through the Bagdad gorge between Morgan and Bruce. The new railroad crossed the Morgan Creek valley on a high trestle next to the abandoned Morgan furnace. Between the trestle and the gorge, several small rock cuts were excavated. Either while making these rock cuts or while digging foundations for the trestle legs, the railroad gang found a vein of quartz which held some amount of gold. The value of the vein was not enough to justify relocating the railroad, so it was ignored and the construction crews moved on.

Michigan State Gazetteer 1881

Ever since the first settlement was established in

94

the 1840s, Marquette was best known as a shipping port for the rich iron mines of Ishpeming and Negaunee. Beginning in its early days, however, Marquette was the site of a number of gold prospects. In 1854 and 1855, Silas C. Smith discovered mineral deposits which carried from $10 to $140 per ton in gold somewhere within the present city limits. Smith had earlier founded a whetstone business, with a quarry in Negaunee and a factory in Marquette (giving Whetstone Brook its name). He later gained fame for his discovery of the Lake Superior Silver Lead Range near Silver Lake. His gold discoveries in the city were apparently too small for profitable mining and were never developed. Iron ore continued to be the main economic mineral of the area.

In 1876, a deposit of low grade iron ore was found west of Marquette, not far from the present Marquette Golf and Country Club. Terrence Moore, who had been president of the Ontonagon Silver Mining Company during the Ontonagon silver boom of the early 1870s, farmed the land adjacent to this discovery. Moore decided to explore his land for a continuation of the vein of iron. Although the iron ore did not extend onto his land, Moore did find a vein of slate which carried pyrite and chalcopyrite. When he showed Silas Smith a specimen of this rock, Smith brought out a sample of rich gold ore from a mine out west. The minerals were nearly identical, prompting Moore to submit samples for assay to Julius Ropes and to an assayer in Pittsburgh, Pennsylvania. The assay

Michigan State Gazetteer 1881

reports came back showing $6 to $25 in gold and silver per ton.

Moore quietly proceeded to test the prospect, eventually sinking a shaft 20 feet into the deposit. Finally, in May 1883, when the opening of the Ropes Gold Mine in Ishpeming had stirred up an interest in gold mining, he decided to organize a stock company to develop the mine. Moore served as treasurer of the new Marquette Gold and Silver Company, with Samuel E. Byrne as president, John Buchanan as vice president, Albert Hornstein as secretary and Thomas Meads as director. The company placed 1,000 shares of stock on the market at 50 cents each to finance development work, and on June 4, 1883, a force of men went to work in the shaft. The directors planned to sink the shaft to at least 70 feet, then start drifting

Captain Moore's steamer the *Smith Moore* Peter White Public Library

and crosscutting in the vein. They also planned to erect a stamp mill, to be run by water power from a nearby stream. The only news ever published about the prospect following these optimistic plans was in July 1883 when it was reported that the miners were still working and that the vein was becoming wider with depth. However, either the gold or capital failed to materialize, and the mine faded into obscurity.

The next chapter in the history of Marquette as a gold mining town began in the fall of 1884. While grading a street for a new residential area near what

is now the corner of High Street and Hewitt Avenue, Captain Smith Moore discovered a deposit of slate and granite laced with two- to four-inch stringers of quartz holding copper ore, iron ore and pyrites. When specimens from the vein were tested, they were found to carry from $4 up to $84 in gold per ton, with traces of silver. Moore, a Great Lakes freighter captain, land developer and owner of the European House Hotel, took a 60-day option on the land from its owner, Peter White, and set a crew of men to work stripping and crosscutting the vein. One of the workmen caused a momentary stir when he uncovered a 30-pound nugget, but when brought to the surface and examined, it turned out to be float copper.

Captain Moore systematically explored the vein, making numerous assays and sending a test lot of the ore to a smelter in Chicago. Most of the assays came back in the $5 to $10 per ton range, encouraging him

The European House, owned by Captain Smith Moore
Peter White Public Library

97

to organize the Euclid Gold Mining Company in late-December 1884. A block of stock was offered for sale at 50 cents per share and was soon sold out. By the following May, a shaft had been sunk 18 feet at the prospect, and specimens assaying up to $160 had been found. Rock from the mine, including much that bore some gold, was hauled away and used in the

construction of basements in Moore's Addition. It was even used to pave the new Prospect Street which ran past the mine.

Richard Crow, the mill superintendent from the Ropes Gold Mine and a highly experienced gold mining man, inspected the prospect in 1885 and expressed his optimism for the development of a paying mine. Moore shared his optimism and announced plans to install either a stamp mill or a Wiswell pulverizer to recover the gold from the rock. Investors had less faith, however, and capital was hard to come by. Captain Moore was forced to seek financial backing outside the local area, and in October he met in Cleveland, Ohio, with investors who financed the purchase of a steam-driven air compressor and power drill. The new equipment allowed the prospect to be

Smith Moore's Gold Mine, near the corner of High St. and Mt. Vernon St. (now Hewitt Ave.) *Peter White Public Library*

opened more rapidly, but no richer or more abundant ore was found.

In March 1886, a large sample of rock was sent to Chicago for treatment by a new process for recovering gold. Although the results of the test were promising enough to bring a group of Chicago investors to Marquette to negotiate a deal, little work was done, and the prospect was soon abandoned. Moore never lost faith in the mine, however, and in 1888 he was still attempting to raise the

funds to reopen the prospect. That fall the Euclid Company called in a five-cent-per-share assessment on its stock, but little money was paid in, and no more exploration was ever done. The shaft and pits were filled in, and homes were built where the boiler house once stood. Smith Moore's gold mine became no more than a page in Marquette's history.

A couple months after Captain Moore's discovery, Marquette grocer John W. Spear took an option and opened a prospect a few hundred feet west of the Euclid Company's. Along with lawyer Dan H. Ball and pharmacist Henry H. Stafford (Julius Ropes' former employer), Spear organized the Marquette Gold Mining Company, with Ball serving as president and Spear as secretary/treasurer. Assays showed $24 per ton in gold and silver, so the company let a contract to sink a 30-foot shaft.

However, almost as soon as the company was organized, the founders became embroiled in controversy. Working without the other directors' knowledge, Spear advertised Marquette Gold Mining Company stock in Detroit and Chicago and sold a large number of shares at 50 cents apiece. As soon as they became aware of Spear's actions, President Ball and Director

Dan H. Ball
Men of Progress

99

DAN. H. BALL.

J. E. BALL.

BALL & BALL,
ATTORNEYS-AT-LAW
206-207-208 NESTER BLK.,
_____MICH.
MARQUETTE,

Stafford resigned, wishing to avoid any association with a possible stock swindle. Stafford and Ball felt that only a limited amount of stock should have been sold, just enough to raise working capital to start mining. They hoped that a rich showing as the mine was developed would enhance the value of the stock and strengthen the company's financial position.

As the shaft was sunk during the winter of 1885, the ore became steadily richer. At 25 feet, samples showed up to $27 per ton in gold and silver. When the shaft reached 30 feet, a crosscut was begun, heading south into the footwall. Ore assaying up to $138 was found, but the rich quartz was only found in narrow stringers. Although the force of miners was doubled in the spring and rich specimens were still found, not enough ore could be mined to treat profitably. By the end of the summer, work at the prospect had ceased.

Although he was disappointed with his former partner's business practices, Henry Stafford retained his faith in Marquette's potential for gold mining. In March 1885, he joined with Richard Blake (who was Dan Ball's bookkeeper) and a Mr. Davis in an exploration a few hundred feet northwest of the Moore prospect. The men found an eight-inch quartz vein which yielded up to $31 in silver and $18 in gold, and organized the Eureka Gold Mining Company. In May, they set 10 men to work sinking a shaft on the vein,

Marquette City Directory

100

planning to go to 60 feet. By the end of the month, they had reached a depth of at least 10 feet, and the vein had widened to two feet. However, the rich surface showings must not have continued at depth, because the prospect was soon given up.

Late in 1885, Marquette County Sheriff Andrew A. Anderson and Ferdinand Bending found a vein of mineralized quartz north of the city. The prospect,

H. H. STAFFORD,
DEALER IN
DRUGS, MEDICINES
FANCY GOODS, BOOKS, STATIONERY,
Prescriptions carefully prepared Day and Night.
Cor. Front and Spring Sts. Marquette, L. S., Mich.

located east of the Lake Superior Powder Company's mill along the Dead River (the present site of the Tourist Park and the municipal hydroelectric plant), gave samples yielding $12 per ton in gold and silver. Anderson and Bending began sinking a shaft, following the vein as it widened from two feet at the surface to seven feet at a depth of 25 feet.

With all the gold mines and prospects being opened up in Ishpeming and Marquette, Daniel H. Merritt of the Iron Bay Foundry saw an opportunity to use his metallurgical expertise to join in the gold boom. In partnership with Captain Bailey and Professor Henry, Merritt established an experimental smelter at the foundry. The "gold saver" was tested on gold ores from the Lake Superior prospect in Ishpeming and from Sheriff Anderson's shaft. It reportedly recovered up to 93 percent of the gold in the ore, a great improvement over the 75 percent recovery

Michigan State Gazetteer 1881

101

rate for the Cornish stamp mill. Despite these promising results, the smelter never progressed beyond the experimental stage. Sheriff Anderson's gold mine likewise never achieved success. The shaft reached a depth of only 35 feet before the mine closed down late in 1885.

Michigan State
Gazetteer 1881

D.H. Merritt
Biographical Record

One of the shortest-lived prospects in Marquette was begun by Ole Oleson, an employee of the Burtis Sawmill. Early in June 1885, Oleson started a small shaft along Lake Street near the Grace Furnace. Assays from the prospect at the base of the hill showed some gold and silver, and Oleson optimistically expected to find something when the shaft reached 40 feet. It is not known if the shaft ever reached that depth, or if Oleson ever found any gold, but he did make the papers again in July. On Saturday the 18th, Oleson set off a blast which sent rocks flying through the windows of a neighboring house, striking the occupant, Mrs. Horne, in the face and wrist. The prospect was apparently shut down a short time later.

Gold mining fever in Marquette was revived in the

late-1890s when the precious metal was found in copper deposits south of the city. The copper range, on what is now known as Migisy Bluff, was discovered in 1888 by Andrew S. Pings. Pings is best known for his brownstone quarry at Mount Mesnard. He was prospecting south of town for a company of local men when he found a vein of copper ore on the NE ¼ of the NW ¼ of Section 1, T47N-R25W. Along with T.C. and W.A. Foard, Peter F. Frei and Oliver Christmas, Pings worked for a while proving up the vein before selling the prospect to Julian Case of Marquette. Case

---

MINES, MINERAL AND TIMBER LANDS

Bought and Sold.

MINES IN MARQUETTE, MENOMINEE and GOGEBIC IRON DISTRICTS

For Sale.

Options for Mining Leases secured on Desirable Lands.

EXPLORATIONS FOR IRON ORE CONDUCTED.

Special attention given to

→ Selecting Iron Lands and Exploring for Iron Ore ←

JULIAN M. CASE,

Marquette, Mich.

---

was a mining man who had made his fortune in iron ore and was also involved in the Verde Antique marble quarry and several gold properties near Ishpeming and on the Gogebic Range. He gave the new copper property his usual vigorous attention, sinking a shaft 18 feet into the vein and shipping a ton of the ore to a smelter in Chicago for testing. The ore, containing chalcopyrite and chalcocite rather than native copper, yielded more than 10.5 percent copper, a very promising result. Unfortunately, Case died before he had a chance to develop the prospect.

Marquette City Directory

After selling the prospect to Case, Andrew Pings continued to explore the Migisy Bluff area. Some distance west of the Case vein, he discovered another copper deposit near the center of Section 2, T47N-R25W. He was able to interest Peter R. Gottstein of Houghton, who obtained an option on the property from its owners, the Harlow family of Marquette, and hired Pings to head up the exploration. Gottstein and Pings sank a test pit and traced the vein onto the adjacent parcel of land, owned by the Iron Cliffs Company. When they were unable to get an option on the Iron Cliffs land, the prospectors abandoned their search, and the veins were forgotten for several years.

In the fall of 1897, explorations were resumed on the copper veins, spurred by reports that smelter tests of ore from the Case vein yielded $12 in gold, six ounces of silver and three percent copper. A wealthy Marquette man, John Munro Longyear, now owned the Case prospect and set a small force of men to work sampling the vein. The Case shaft was located near the center of Section 1, T47N-R25W. Longyear's crews traced the vein several hundred feet and sank a new shaft. A test of some 20 tons of ore at the Chicago and Aurora Smelting and Refining Company in Aurora, Illinois, showed less than one percent copper, however, and the prospect was closed down early in 1898. The shaft had reached a depth of 40 feet into the 10-foot wide vein.

Meanwhile, James Wilkinson, a Marquette banker, had obtained options on the former Gottstein and Pings vein from both the Harlows and the Iron Cliffs Company. Specimens from the Wilkinson prospect assayed as high as $10.33 per ton in gold, with 1.5 percent copper and a small amount of silver. In No-

John Munro
Longyear
Men of Progress

vember 1897, Wilkinson sold his property rights to a group of Chicago investors headed by John W. Ludwig, with Pings retaining a minor interest. The Ludwig group set four miners to work under the direction of Captain Josiah Broad, an experienced mining captain and former Marquette County sheriff, and sank two shafts east of Gottstein's test pit. One shaft, on the Harlow property, reached a depth of 40 feet,

J. M. LONGYEAR,
BROKER IN
Michigan Mineral and Timber Lands,
MARQUETTE, MICH.

Agent for the Lands of the Lake Superior Ship Canal, Railway and Iron Company.

600,000 ACRES FOR SALE OR LEASE

Lands Sold; Taxes Paid; Titles Examined; Defective Titles Adjusted; Lands Examined for Timber and Minerals; Lands Located at State and Government Offices.

Iron Ore Lands to Lease on Royalty.

PINE AND HARDWOOD TIMBER FOR SALE.
REFERENCES GIVEN IF DESIRED.

while the shaft on the Iron Cliffs land was sunk 25 feet. By January 1898, eight to 10 miners were working at the site, a boarding house had been built and George Spencer had taken over as superintendent.

Early in 1898, Wallace Kirk, the son of a wealthy soap manufacturer from Chicago, came to Marquette and bought out the Ludwig Company's interest in the prospect. Kirk increased the work force to 20 men and had an addition built onto the boarding house to accommodate them. It seemed that this infusion of money from the young millionaire was just what was needed to put the mine on a paying basis. When it came time to pay the bills, however, Kirk was always out of town, and when he finally did meet the payroll, his check bounced. When Kirk never returned, the miners all quit and the prospect closed again, this time for good.

Captain Martin Daniels may have seemed like an unlikely prospector, being a Great Lakes ship captain rather than a mining captain. For more than 20 years he had sailed Lake Superior, often carrying cargos of black powder and high explosives from the Mar-

Marquette City Directory 1886-7

105

quette Powder Works to the copper mines of the Keweenaw Peninsula. As the master of the small schooner *Tom Boy*, he nearly lost his life to the lake when, on August 1, 1880, the heavily laden vessel sprang a leak during a storm and sank. Captain Daniels and his lone crewman escaped in the ship's yawl and were picked up by a passing steamer. Within a month, the captain purchased a new vessel, the *Mystic*, and continued his hazardous voyages.

Some of his customers' enthusiasm for mineral exploration must have rubbed off on Daniels, for in the late-1890s, after retiring from the lakes, he began

JAMES M. WILKINSON,
BANKER
Transacts a General Banking and Exchange Business.
SPECIAL ATTENTION GIVEN TO MERCANTILE COLLECTIONS.
MARQUETTE, - - MICHIGAN.

prospecting along the lake between Marquette and the Copper Country. In the winter of 1897-98, he discovered a vein of native silver about 18 miles up the shore from Marquette, apparently in the Saux Head region. That same winter, he also found a deposit of conglomerate rock containing three percent copper on the NE ¼ of Section 5, T49N-R26W. This is one of the only deposits of native copper ever found in Marquette County. Most of the other discoveries in this area have been copper ores, usually chalcopyrite. Along with Samuel York and John Tebo, Daniels started an exploration shaft, named the "Francis A" for his youngest child. By the end of 1898, a pool of Marquette businessmen had bought control of the prospect and set 10 men to work, deepening the shaft to 20 feet. The copper petered out, however, and the

Michigan State Gazetteer 1891-2

prospect was abandoned.

Captain Daniels, meanwhile, had directed his explorations a couple of miles to the north onto Section 30, T50N-R26W, where a homesteader had reported finding placer gold in a creek in 1891. Daniels soon found a four-foot-wide vein containing copper, silver and a trace of gold. Here he sank two test shafts, one at the bottom of a small hill and the other near the top. Assays showing up to 24 percent copper and $1.75 per ton in silver were rich enough to encourage Daniels to form a stock company in early 1899 and to offer 20,000 shares at 25 cents each. Treasurer George Barnes, a bank cashier, and secretary F. Stuart Byrne, a bookkeeper for the LS&I Railroad, handled the new company's finances. Revenues from the stock sale were used to hire miners from the Copper Country to deepen the No. 1 shaft at the base of the hill.

For the next three years, work was carried on sporadically as capital became available. Finally, on Christmas Eve 1901, the miners struck what they felt was the main body of ore at a depth of 30 feet, where the vein widened to 12 feet. Although the copper content had decreased to eight percent, the gold value was now $1.79 per ton. With this promising showing, stock prices rose to 50 cents per share.

By the summer of 1902, the shaft was 50 feet deep, and crosscutting to test the width of the ore body was begun. Copper now made up only four percent of the

Marquette City Directory 1886-7

ore, but the gold was worth $3.75 and the silver $4.75 per ton of ore. The stockholders decided to reorganize the company as a development syndicate, issuing 1,000 shares at $100 par value. Peter Primeau and lawyer Charles F. Button joined Barnes as trustees, while George Hodgkins took over as secretary.

At 60 feet, the miners struck an even richer body of ore, which they concluded must be the true "main body." An assay by F. D. Tower of the Carp River Furnace showed 9.2 percent copper with $13.72 in gold and $3.99 in silver per ton. A steam hoist and water pump were added, and the shaft was deepened to 72 feet. Here the sinking stopped, while Daniels and his associates renewed their options on the property. In December 1902, the company was again reorganized, this time as The Original Sauk's Head Mine Limited. The company offered 100,000 shares of stock for sale at 10 cents per share to finance further exploration and development work. Button served as chairman, Barnes continued as treasurer and Alfred Archambeau succeeded Byrne as secretary. Louis Grabower and Joseph Vertin joined as managers.

Work resumed at the mine in February 1903, with eight miners working. Little news of the prospect was published over the next year. Finally, in April 1904, the company bought the E ½ of the SE ¼ of the section, which the company's officers believed to carry the elusive "main vein," from the Rublein family. Apparently no main body of rich ore was ever found,

Gazetteer of Marquette County 1889

and ownership of the land eventually reverted to the

Rubleins. Today the shafts lie water-filled and forgotten, silent witnesses to Captain Daniels' dreams of golden riches.

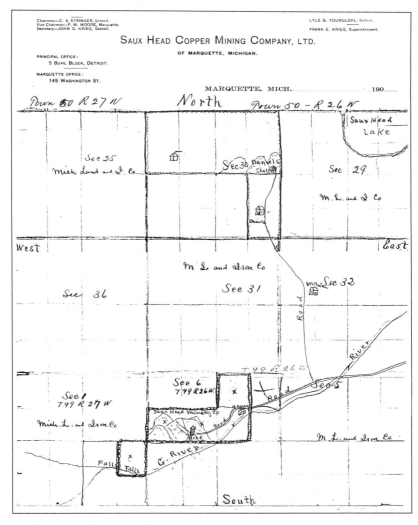

After the "Francis A" prospect on Section 5 was abandoned in 1899, members of the Krieg family of Marquette began prospecting in the area. They traced the Daniels vein more than a mile to the west onto Section 6, T49N-R26W, where they owned 160 acres of

Frank Krieg's map of the Krieg's and Daniels' mines

Fred Rydholm

109

land and held options on another 280. In November 1899, they formed the Saux Head Copper Mining and Development Company Limited. Based in Detroit, the company was led by Captain John Considine Jr. of Detroit, president; Eugene J. Krieg of Marquette, vice president; John G. Krieg of Detroit, secretary; and George R. Purdon of Detroit, treasurer. Frank E. Krieg of Marquette served as superintendent. The company announced its plans to sell enough stock to begin development that winter, but work did not start in earnest until 1901, when an inclined shaft was sunk 14 feet before being shut down for the winter.

Work was resumed in the spring of 1902, and the eight-foot-square shaft was deepened to 38 feet over the summer. The ore had richened steadily with depth, the gold value increasing from $4.16 per ton at 15 feet to $125 per ton at the bottom. In September, the company was reorganized and renamed the Saux Head Copper Mining Company Limited. Detroit insurance agent Charles A. Stringer took over as president, with Charles Krieg as treasurer and Marquette lawyer Francis M. Moore succeeding Eugene Krieg, who had died late in 1899, as vice president. The new company decided to equip the shaft with a steam hoist, to be housed in a log building along with the blacksmith shop. The hoisting engine and other equipment were brought in over the wagon road from Marquette, but the boiler was too large for the rock cut at Sugarloaf. Hauling the boiler over the rocks around the cut took several days. By the end of 1902, the shaft was down 54 feet, and a drift had been driven 12 feet into the vein. Assays from the shaft and drift showed gold values up to $195.70 and silver as high as $12.12 per ton.

In the spring of 1904, the Saux Head Company hired expert mining engineer John A. Knight to supervise the prospect. Eight to 10 men were employed at the mine, and the shaft eventually reached a depth of about 120 feet. Assays of ore from near the bottom of the shaft in October 1904 showed $10.50 to $13 in gold and up to $75 in silver per ton, but water seeping into the workings from the nearby Big Garlic River finally forced the prospect to be abandoned that winter.

Frank Krieg stayed on at his homestead about a half a mile from the mine after the shaft flooded. In 1905 he took a job running the Northern Lumber Company's general store at the newly built sawmill town of Birch, located between the mine and Saux Head Lake. With his brother Charles, he continued to work at gold mining. They sank two more small shafts, then decided to attempt to hit the ore body by driving an adit into the hillside. The Kriegs drove the adit about 50 feet into the rock without finding gold before giving up for good.

Around 1891, after the closing of his mine near the Dead River, Ephraim Coon settled north of the small community of Clowry, west of Ishpeming. Here, on the SE ¼ of Section 10, T48N-R29W, he started another shaft on a vein of gold-bearing quartz. Local

legend says that a stranger named Hawkins mysteriously appeared and helped Coon to build a windmill on an 80-foot tripod to pump the water from the shaft. Just as the windmill neared completion, however, Hawkins disappeared as suddenly as he had arrived, leaving the machinery unfinished. Coon apparently never continued the mine.

Saux Head Copper Mining Company Limited (Krieg's Gold Mine) *Superior View Studio*

In 1927, Martin Suneson bought 120 acres of land in the SW ¼ of Section 8, T46N-R29W, near the village of Republic. Over the next few years, he explored the land and diamond drilled, finding a vein of quartz two to four feet wide which he claimed carried up to $4 per ton in gold. However, the vein was too small and low grade to pay, and in the 1960s, when the Cleveland Cliffs Iron Company built its Republic iron mine concentrator and pellet plant, the new mine workings and buildings obliterated all signs of Suneson's prospect.

CHAPTER SEVEN

Baraga, Iron and Dickinson County Prospects

E ver since the death of Douglass Houghton in 1845, rumors have persisted that his original gold find was located in the Huron Mountains of northern Marquette and Baraga counties. Even after the discovery of the Ishpeming Gold Range and the opening of the Ropes Gold Mine, prospectors continued to search this rugged country for gold veins. Late in 1884, reports began to be heard of a new gold mine somewhere between L'Anse and Michigamme, with rumors of ore worth $80 per ton. Finally, in May 1885, W.J. Ray of Ishpeming revealed the location of his prospect. Situated high on a divide in Section 17, T49N-R32W, in Baraga County, the vein had been traced 500 feet along the surface. Five assays of the vein rock averaged $16 per ton in gold, and Ray announced plans to form a mining company, hire miners and build a mill equipped with a Wiswell pulverizer. With the secret of its location revealed, public interest in the prospect dwindled and little mention of it was made in the media. It is unknown if the company ever came to be or how much work was done.

In 1882, before the discovery of the Michigan vein, George Grummett had found a gold vein on Section 20, T47N-R32W, in Baraga County. On the shores of what was then called Horricon Lake (later called Grummett Lake and now known as Ned Lake), he found the quartz vein in at least five spots. The lode ranged from six to 60 feet wide, with assays showing up to $30 per ton in gold. On the basis of this find,

he started the Grummett Gold and Silver Mining Company and purchased more than 260 acres, nearly the entire west side of the lake. Grummett served as president, with W.S. Hill as secretary and Anson B. Miner as treasurer. A force of miners was set to work under Captain Henry Davis in early 1885, but a lack of investors forced the company to close down the prospect. By that fall, Grummett had interested Detroit parties, and in the spring of 1886 he sold a one-half interest in the property to E.H. McGinley of Lower Michigan. How much work was done by McGinley is not known.

By 1906, gold mining was but a memory to most of Michigan, but the Grummett Gold and Silver Mining Company was still in existence and proposing to renew its explorations on the Michigamme prospect. At the company's 1906 stockholders meeting, a 2.5-cent-per-share assessment was called to finance explorations. Over the summer, George Grummett and his sons returned to the prospect and reopened the three old shafts, which had been flooded since a logging company had dammed the outlet to the lake some years before. With the logging finished and the dam opened, Grummett was able to clean out the shafts, each of which was about 16 feet deep, and take samples of the ore in the vein. With specimens of free gold on display, the Grummett company offered the property for sale at a reasonable price, but no buyers came forward, and the prospect was again abandoned. In 1913, the property was sold to Randall P. Bronson, who had previously been involved in the B&M Gold Company, but no further work was done.

About seven miles east of the Grummett prospect,

George Grummett
Marguerite Grummett Bergdahl

the Hancock Iron Mining Company was exploring for iron ore in 1888. One of the officers of the company was John R. Gordon of Hancock, who had found a gold vein on the Dead River Gold Range two years before. The Hancock Company succeeded in finding a promising vein of iron ore on the N ½ of Section 16, T47N-R31W, near Fence Lake. When the Michigan Gold Mine began to produce fabulously rich specimens that fall, the company's explorer, Captain John Marks, turned his attention to a vein of mineralized quartz which had been uncovered during the course of the exploration. Sinking a shaft through 25 feet of overburden to the vein, Captain Marks' crew found it to carry free gold. As the shaft was deepened, the vein grew wider and richer. Gold mining experts reported that the vein compared favorably with those in the Ishpeming area. The Hancock Iron Company purchased a diamond drill rig and set to work looking for extensions of the vein, but must have failed in its endeavor, since no more was heard from this company.

Midway between the Grummett and Hancock prospects is what is rumored to be another gold mine. On the SE ¼ of the SE ¼ of Section 14, T47N-R32W, unknown parties drove a timbered adit some 50 feet into a gravel bank. The miners laid wooden rails and used a tram car to haul the ore (or gold-bearing gravel) out of the mine. Today the prospect is abandoned, the adit has caved in and the tram car has been hauled away.

On some old maps of Baraga County, the notation "Old Gold Pit" is shown on the northern part of Section 10, T50N-R30W. Ownership records show that the NE ¼ of the section was purchased from the government by James Dwyer in 1885. Dwyer, who also owned a gold prospect near the Michigan Gold Mine, sold shares in the property to timber baron Timothy Nester, Henry Atkinson and Peter White. The property was later bought by mining engineer James Jopling and was eventually acquired by the Cleveland Cliffs Iron Company in 1901. CCI geologist C.M. Farnham, in a 1907 field report, described an exploration shaft sunk on a six-inch quartz vein by the Mar-

The Grummett Gold and Silver Mining Co. stock certificate

No. 205 · STATE OF MICHIGAN · 20 Shares

THE GRUMMETT GOLD AND SILVER MINING CO.

Incorporated Nov 8d, 1884

CAPITAL STOCK 2500,000 · 100,000 SHARES, $25 EACH.

quette Gold and Silver Company in this area. It is not known if this company, which had worked Terrence Moore's gold prospect in Marquette in 1883, actually explored this property or if Dwyer and his associates operated under a similar title. In any case, the shallow shaft did not yield any quantity of gold.

In September 1888, a group of Copper Country men organized the Huron Mountain Exploring and Mining Company. The company was formed to explore and develop a vein of gold-bearing quartz which had been found by Thomas Dooling and Joseph C. Foley at an undisclosed location northeast of L'Anse in the Huron Mountains. Dooling served as president of the company, John F. Ryan as secretary and treasurer and Foley, W.S. Cleaves and Martin Conway served as directors. The company was capitalized at $1 million: 40,000 shares at $25 par value. Information as to the location of the prospect and the extent of the company's work is lacking.

The same year, John B. Belanger found a mineralized vein on the SW ¼ of Section 36, T52N-R30W, near the east branch of the Huron River. Belanger

Grummett Stock
Marguerite Grummett Bergdahl

traced the 15-foot vein 100 feet on the surface and claimed that an assay of the rock showed $5 in gold, $10 in silver and $10 in zinc per ton. Belanger never succeeded in opening a mine on the vein, but some time later the landowner, Christopher Ching, sold the parcel to John Thompson of Chicago as "valuable mineral land."

In 1914, Thompson was prospecting for manganese on his property and sent samples to Chicago for testing. Late in the year, the report came to him that some of the samples contained economic quantities of vanadium, which, like manganese, is used in making high-strength steel. Thompson put a crew to work at the prospect, building a snug winter camp and a blacksmith shop. By the end of the year, the men had sunk an 18-foot shaft, which Thompson's associate, George W. McGhee, named the Bughole Mine. They also started another shaft nearby, and although it only reached a depth of four feet, they optimistically called it the Mohatin Hills Mine. McGhee wrote a glowing report on the mine, which was published in *Mining and Engineering World.* The article prompted the Michigan Commissioner of Mines and Mineral Statistics, R.C. Allen, to assign Professor W.E. Hopper of the Michigan School of Mines in Houghton to investigate the prospect. Hopper visited the site and took samples, but found the vein to contain nothing more than galena and small amounts of pyrite and chalcopyrite. The "mines" apparently closed down soon afterward, with much less fanfare than had accompanied their opening.

Orrin Robinson, an early mineral explorer, found gold at several locations in Baraga and Iron counties. Robinson felt that the numerous quartz veins crossing the rock formations near the upper reaches of the Sturgeon River were promising for gold. Around the turn of the century, he sank a six-foot shaft on one of these veins and took out samples assaying from a trace to $2 per ton in gold. The vein proved too small to mine. Some years earlier, Jim Holliday, a Native American from L'Anse, had found a mineralized vein while trapping near Perch Lake in northern Iron

County. He invited Robinson to inspect the vein. The men traveled by foot and canoe from Houghton to Perch Lake, where they relocated Holliday's vein near the north end of the lake. Assays of samples from the vein showed plumbago (graphite) and a trace of gold.

Other locations in Baraga County were searched for gold in 1897 and 1898. Near Covington, an old explorer named Fred Schonnaway took an option on lands belonging to the Duluth, South Shore and Atlantic Railroad. He sank a 10-foot shaft, revealing rich-looking rock, but no assays were made. At about the same time, a lumberman brought in samples of quartz carrying free gold worth $10 per ton. Other reports quoted assay reports as high as $12,000 per ton, but no locations were made public, and little more was heard of gold mining in Baraga County.

Dickinson County on the Menominee Iron Range was the site of numerous iron ore mines. In the late-1800s, it was also the site of several gold prospects. During the summer of 1885, a small shaft was sunk some three miles northeast of Norway, near Pine Creek. One assay of a sample from the shaft showed $60 per ton in gold, while another showed $6 in gold plus $1 in silver. Apparently there was too little gold for mining, but enough to keep interest up, for the vein was still being tested more than 10 years later.

In 1888, John L. Buell located a vein of gold-bearing rock on the banks of the Menominee River, south of the present town of East Kingsford. Buell was joined in the exploration of the prospect by Ben Marchand of Quinnesec and Joseph Flescheim of Menominee. Located on Lot 4, Section 7 and Lot 1, Section 8, T39N-R30W, the land was owned by the

Orrin W. Robinson
Biographical Record

118

Menominee Mining Company and held under option by Hugh McLaughlin. An assay of some of the vein rock by Julius Ropes showed $72 in gold and $10 in silver per ton, but the six-inch vein was too small to work profitably.

During the mid-1930s, a couple of men from Iron Mountain found a gold vein near the section line between Sections 19 and 30, T41N-R30W, about seven miles north of Iron Mountain. The quartz vein, which carried pyrite and chalcopyrite, also showed assay values from a trace to about an ounce of gold per ton. The men were unable to raise capital to work the prospect in the midst of the Great Depression, and so the vein was forgotten.

CHAPTER EIGHT

Gogebic Range Gold Mines

Apart from the Ishpeming area, the only other concentration of gold prospects in Michigan occurred in Gogebic county. Early in the county's history, several explorers were reported to have found gold and silver. A Dr. Kane and Mr. Purdy from Jackson, Michigan, as well as I.D. Bush of Detroit, were said to have found the precious metals at undisclosed locations in the county. A Mr. McKellar (probably Peter McKellar, well-known geologist of Fort William, Ontario) reportedly found native gold in several townships in Range 46 West. Galena carrying small amounts of silver was found in a number of prospects a few miles west of Lake Gogebic in the early 1880s, finds that are recalled today by the names of Prospector's Creek and Galena Creek. None of these discoveries proved to be rich or extensive enough to mine.

In the spring of 1884, explorers found a vein of sandstone carrying up to $215 per ton in silver on the S ½ of the SE ¼ of Section 10, T47N-R45W, near the south line of the section. The vein was also traced onto the northern edge of Section 14. Later that year, a similar formation was found on Section 15. Again, none of the veins was extensive enough for mining.

Captain James Tobin was exploring about six miles west of Lake Gogebic early in 1884 when he found a vein of gold-bearing quartz in the N ½ of the NE ¼ of Section 28, T47N-R43W. The vein, which was seven feet wide, carried gold in pyrite and copper ore and assayed $20 per ton. The Summit Exploration, Mining and Manufacturing Company, which was led by George M. Wakefield of Oshkosh, Wisconsin, owned the land and hired Tobin to sink a shaft and test the vein. At a depth of seven feet, the bottom of the shaft was sampled across its width, yielding an average of $20.80 per ton in gold and $9.50 in silver. The shaft was carried down to 27 feet before the

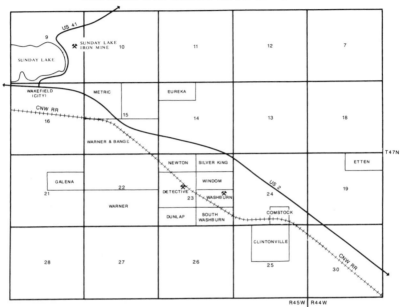

prospect was closed for the winter. Although the company announced plans to reopen the prospect in the spring, it seems the vein had pinched out at depth and no further work was done.

In the summer of 1885, Samuel Moreau found a two-foot vein of quartz carrying galena and pyrite about four miles southeast of Sunday Lake in the NE ¼ of Section 25, T47N-R45W. The vein assayed up to $15 per ton in gold and silver, but pinched out at a depth of 18 feet.

Around 1880, P. Mitchell of Ontonagon found a body of iron ore near the boundary between Sections 12 and 13, T46N-R42W. Mitchell sank a series of test pits, tracing the deposit along its east-west trend. The

The Gogebic Gold Range
NMU Cartographic Lab

122

land belonged to the Agogebic Exploring, Mining and Manufacturing Company, which, like the Summit, was owned by investors led by George M. Wakefield. In February 1885, while exploring for iron ore at the Mitchell location, the Agogebic Company's crews found a vein of gold-bearing quartz in their 85-foot-deep shaft. An assay of the rock

showed $113.63 per ton in gold plus $12.10 per ton in silver. Although the vein proved too small for development, its discovery did prompt a boom in exploration of the adjoining sections.

The main beneficiaries of the boom seemed to be the Summit and Agogebic companies. The two companies owned 60,000 acres in the Gogebic area, much of it in the vicinity of the gold finds, and they did a good business selling exploration options. Near the Mitchell location, on the NW ¼ of the NW ¼ of Section 13, J.M. Case of Marquette sank a six-foot shaft into a quartz vein mineralized with copper ore. It produced samples assaying up to $182.81 per ton in gold and silver. Captain Tobin and several other prospectors reported gold finds in Sections 12, 13 and 14, but none of these veins proved to be large enough for mining.

With the rapid growth of the Gogebic Range iron mines in the mid-1880s, George Wakefield saw the need for a new town on the shores of Sunday Lake. The village of Wakefield was platted in 1886 and soon became a thriving business center. Businessmen from Waupaca County, Wisconsin, were among the first to settle there. L.D. Goldberg of Marion, Wisconsin, opened a general store, selling groceries, clothing and miners' and lumbermen's supplies. His brother, B.M. Goldberg, set up a legal practice along with Walter Goodland. Goldberg and Goodland also published the *Iron Herald*

new village's first newspaper, the *Wakefield Bulletin.*

Originally, the Gogebic Range was part of Ontonagon County, but in 1887 Gogebic County was incorporated, with Bessemer as its county seat. Dozens of companies were formed to explore for iron ore, taking options on 80-acre parcels all along the presumed trend of the rich iron ore formation. A great many of these options were sold by W.W. Warner, a dealer in options and mining stocks.

In the spring of 1887, George Miracle was exploring for iron ore on the E ½ of the NE ¼ of Section 25, T47N-R45W, on an option he held in partnership with L.D. Goldberg. Prospecting in the same quarter section where Sam Moreau had made his gold find, Miracle encountered a narrow seam of soft, decomposed rock which carried sulfide minerals. The seam grew wider as the exploratory shaft went deeper, and a sample was assayed, yielding $16.00 per ton in silver and $6.60 in gold. The vein was traced some 275 feet along the surface, and a shaft was sunk 18 feet.

With the promising showing of precious metals at the Miracle prospect, several exploration companies decided that if their options didn't hold iron ore, perhaps they did have gold and silver. Parties from Clintonville, Wisconsin, including Dr. J. Finney, the town's mayor, organized the Clintonville Mining and Exploring Company in May 1887 to explore two 80-acre parcels just west of the Miracle option. Other investors included Walter Goodland and B.M.

Gogebic Range Directory 1888

124

Goldberg of Wakefield, and N. Etten, F. Nosack, J.A. Hickock and C.C. Spearbracker of Clintonville. Spear-bracker served as president, Hickock was secretary and Finney was the treasurer. The company's option included the E ½ of the NW ¼ and the W ½ of the NE ¼ of Section 25. The Clintonville company soon found a vein of silver ore which Goldberg and Goodland's *Wakefield Bulletin* touted as "large and valuable." Samples from the lode were sent to Chicago for analysis. Although the Clintonville management did not make public the results of these assays, they did proceed to sink a shaft. They announced plans to go to 65 feet, then start drifting, confident of striking the silver-bearing vein.

Mayor Finney and N. Etten were also officers in the Etten Mining Company. E. Brix of Clintonville was the president, with Etten serving as secretary and Finney as treasurer. The Etten company explored the N ½ of the NE ¼ of Section 19, T47N-R44W, a mile northeast of the Clintonville Prospect without finding paying quantities of gold, silver or iron ore.

The most significant gold and silver strike on the Gogebic Range came in the spring of 1887 when W.W. Warner found several small silver-bearing veins on the N ½ of the SE ¼ of Section 23, T47N-R45W. Having immediately secured an option on the property, Warner soon assigned his rights to the Washburn Mining Company, which was formed by investors from Minneapolis and New York, including G.H. Washburn, president; A.D. Westby, secretary; and Captain D.F. Strobeck, treasurer. Warner retained a one-quarter interest in the property and joined with Strobeck, the company's mining captain, in prospecting the veins. The veins were found to come together into a central ore body, where Warner and Strobeck started a shaft. Assays of the galena- and pyrite-bearing rock from the shaft yielded from $8.49 to $138.48 per ton in silver with a trace of gold. As the shaft went deeper, the assay reports became richer, and Captain Strobeck reported finding free gold in "sugar quartz" in the shaft.

Warner's mining option and real estate business

grew rapidly as the gold fever took hold in the fall of 1887. Minnesota investors rushed to form mining companies and buy options anywhere near the gold and silver finds. Warner was ready to serve them, but, the local paper noted, "W.W. Warner cannot locate land situated on the gold and silver formation fast enough

W. W. WARNER & Co.

— DEALERS IN —

REAL ESTATE

AND

Mining Options.

SILVER OPTIONS and STOCK

A SPECIALTY.

A Silver Formation Guaranteed to be LOCATED on Every Option Furnished by us, or Money Refunded

All Legal Papers Executed with Neatness and Dispatch.

Notary Public   and   Collections.

WAKEFIELD,   MICH.

to supply companies formed to operate thereon."

The Detective Mining Company was formed by Minneapolis and St. Paul parties to work the S ½ of the NW ¼ and the N ½ of the SW ¼ of Section 23, west of the Washburn. Investors included W.M. Whitney of Chicago, president; C.S. Northrop of St. Paul,

Wakefield Bulletin

secretary; and J.A. Northrop of Minneapolis, treasurer. The company claimed to have both the Clintonville and Washburn veins crossing its property and cited assays of surface specimens showing $2.65 per ton in silver, with a trace of gold.

Minneapolis investors also organized the Dunlap Mining Company and took an option on the 80 acres adjoining the Detective property on the south, the S ½ of the SW ¼ of Section 23. Frank G. Turnquist served as president, and John A. Turnquist was secretary and treasurer. The property showed a promising vein of quartz.

A.D. Westby, the secretary of the Washburn company, obtained an option on the N ½ of the NW ¼ of Section 23, north of the Detective. He assigned the option to the Newton Mining Company, which was owned by investors from Boston and Minneapolis, including William Leonard, president; L.O. Thayer, secretary; and O.S. Thayer, treasurer.

Just north of the Washburn property on the S ½ of the NE ¼ of Section 23, the Windom Gold and Silver Mining Company set men to work exploring. Along with the Detective, Dunlap and Newton companies, the Windom's absentee owners left operation of the prospect to Captain Strobeck.

The Windom prospect was bordered on the north by the property of the Silver King Mining Company. The company was formed by J.A. McCluskey, president; J.A. Northrop, secretary; and C.S. Northrop, treasurer. Operations were begun under the supervision of Captain Graham, an old western explorer.

With this influx of capital to the region in the summer of 1887, George Miracle and L.D. Goldberg decided to form a stock company to work their Miracle prospect. They incorporated the Wakefield Gold and Silver Company and offered 1,000 shares of stock. W.W. Warner was one of the first to purchase a large block of stock. Miracle was elected president of the new company, with C.M. Harrington as vice president, A.F. Olmstead as secretary and Edward Copps as treasurer. In July 1887, Olmstead took samples to Ishpeming for assay by Julius Ropes. These

127

specimens, from a depth of 28 feet in the shaft, showed $15 per ton in gold. Other specimens were found to contain up to $100 per ton in silver. Over the next few months, the shaft was sunk to a depth of 60 feet, at which depth the lode was 16 to 36 inches wide. Arrangements were made to ship the ore from the mine to a smelter in Newport, Kentucky.

The prospects for silver and gold mining on the Gogebic Range seemed promising enough in late-1887 that officials of the Washburn and Detective companies decided to buy a small smelting furnace to extract the metals from their ores. Shipping ore to the smelter in Kentucky for reduction cost $8 per ton plus transportation. By purchasing a Hartsfeld portable furnace for about $20,000, the mining companies could smelt the ore themselves at a cost of $4 per ton, Captain Strobeck claimed. The furnace seemed to be a fail-safe investment: if the gold and silver prospects didn't pan out, the furnace could supposedly be used to make pig iron from the local iron ore.

Captain Strobeck, A.D. Westby of the Washburn Mining Company and C.B. Holmes incorporated the South Washburn Mining and Smelting Company early in 1888 to buy and operate the smelter. The furnace was to be built on the S ½ of the SE ¼ of Section 23. The company also started an adit and a shaft into a bluff on its property and struck rock reported to be *Gogebic Range Directory 1888* worth up to $60 per ton.

By the end of 1887, W.W. Warner had sunk the Washburn shaft to 40 feet and reported that the vein was still growing wider and richer. His own business was thriving, and his ads now proclaimed "Silver Options and Stock a Specialty. A Silver Formation Guaranteed to be Located on Every Option Furnished by us, or Money Refunded."

However, some of the other prospects were not faring so well. At the Clintonville Mining and Exploring Company's prospect the shaft had reached 65 feet, but pay rock was not to be found. A 20-foot drift to the west likewise failed to show up the elusive vein, and the investors gave up on the mine. A quarter mile to the east, the Wakefield Company, too, seemed to be having trouble locating pay rock. The Dunlap Company, which had been sinking on a vein of sugar quartz, was still looking in vain for any strong indications of gold or silver. Except for initial assays of 47 cents to $13.19 per ton in silver from surface specimens, the Newton Mining Company never did report finding anything more valuable than "very promising quartz and greenstone." The Detective and Silver King prospects were shut down over the winter. By March 1888, C.S. Northrop, who had been the secretary of the Detective and treasurer of the Silver King, was president of both and was trying to make arrangements to reopen the prospects, apparently without success.

W.W. Warner, ever the promoter, was not about to let the boom die down. He personally took over as manager of the Wakefield property and started sinking a second shaft. He began to refer to the first, 60-foot shaft as a "test pit" and confidently planned to sink the new shaft to 100 feet, then crosscut to determine the width of the vein. Warner also found new owners for the Clintonville prospect, selling it to the Comstock Gold and Silver Company. The Comstock Company took over the eastern 80 acres of the Clintonville option and added the 40 acres adjacent on the north, the SW ¼ of the SE ¼ of Section 24. Warner managed the prospect for the company and declared that the vein in which the Clintonville shaft

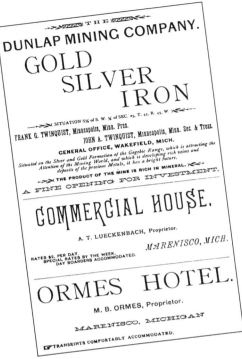

was sunk was merely a feeder, and that the "main vein" would be struck by drifting to the north. The Windom prospect, too, was sold to new owners. Its Minneapolis owners had given it only a cursory exploration before selling it to another group of Twin Cities investors, who renamed it the North Washburn. Captain Strobeck retained his position as manager of the property.

By July 1888, the shaft on the Washburn Mining Company property had reached a depth of 60 feet, and a drift had been started to the east. Assays of the vein rock ranged from $3 to $28 and averaged $18 per ton. Apparently the South Washburn Company never built its smelting furnace, for late in 1888, the Washburn company, now known as the Washburn Mining and Milling Company, built a mill to crush and grind the ore and separate the silver and gold by amalgamation with mercury. The mill, which began operation in November 1888, employed a Wiswell pulverizer to finely grind the gold ore. Rather than amalgamating the gold and silver with mercury in the Wiswell machine as was usually done, the ground rock was fed into a pair of centrifugal pans where it was given a final grinding and mixed with several chemicals. After the mixture was heated by steam, it was fed into another pan where mercury was added to recover the gold. The mine and mill employed some 35 men and ran day and night. Dr. N. Lehnen of St. Paul was the

Gogebic Range Directory 1888 mining engineer.

Although many of the other prospects had failed, the apparent success of the Washburn kept investors interested in the potential fortunes to be made in precious metals in the Wakefield area. W.W. Warner located another gold- and silver-bearing vein on the NW ¼ of Section 15 in the summer of 1888. The Metric Gold and Silver Company was formed to operate the prospect. The company sank a 40-foot shaft on the vein, but it is not known what success they may have had.

Even though the Windom and North Washburn companies had failed to find pay rock on their land, W.W. Warner was able to interest a third company in a newly discovered vein on this property. The Hurley (Wisconsin) *Tribune* reported in January 1889 that, ''At the Minneapolis and Gogebic Mining Company's property, adjoining the Washburn's on the north, a new and very rich vein of gold- and silver-bearing quartz has been shown up or discovered through the means of a new device or mineral-rod, invented and controlled by Capt. W.W. Warner, manager of the Comstock mine, who has located all the veins and shafts of the Washburn properties. This vein on the Minneapolis property was located by the instrument at night, and on doing some stripping next day the quartz vein was discovered to be literally full of galena and silver ore. A fair sample of the quartz was assayed and ran more than $50 per ton in silver, with traces of gold. It will pay mining men to have their properties examined by Mr. Warner before sinking when there are no indications on surface, as the instrument used is pretty certain to give the indications of mineral if any exist.''

The Washburn mill was able to treat only 12 tons of rock per day, being limited by the small capacity of the Wiswell pulverizer, but the company confidently planned to add 100 heads of Cornish stamps, an air compressor and power drills and to sink the shaft to 400 feet with drifts every 50 feet. However, the Washburn never produced any appreciable amount of bullion, shutting down in August 1889. The involved process of extracting the gold was ap-

131

parently too expensive, and the vein was too narrow to be worked at a profit. The shaft only reached a depth of 100 feet with a single 40-foot drift, and drifting and crosscutting in the South Washburn adit totaled only 120 feet.

Warner also participated in several other explorations. He did some prospecting on the S ½ of Section 15 (in partnership with Nick Bangs of Antigo, Wisconsin) and on the S ½ of Section 22, in both cases reporting galena with silver. He also explored on Section 21 and was reported to have sunk two shafts to 15 and 35 feet. A resident of the SW ¼ of the NE ¼ of this section presently uses an old shaft as his well, which he reports to be 80 to 90 feet deep. The Galena Mining Company explored on the S ½ of the NE ¼ of the section and reported finding silver, lead and iron.

About 10 miles north of Ironwood on Section 32, T49N-R47W, George Triplett prospected for copper, silver and gold. Triplett worked for several years sinking test pits and driving adits with unknown results.

Other companies which prospected for gold on the Gogebic Range in Michigan included the Eureka Company, located on the N ½ of the NW ¼ of Section 14, T47N-R45W, and the Section Twenty-Five Company. Little is known about these other companies, but they are all part of the story of the short-lived gold rush on the Gogebic Range.

CHAPTER NINE

Placer Mining

I n prospecting for gold, the " '49ers" of the California gold rush would wash gravel from stream beds in pans and sluices to extract the metal deposited there by erosion. As these placer deposits played out, the prospectors followed the rivers upstream, looking for the "mother lode," the gold-bearing bedrock from which the secondary deposits had been eroded.

Mineral explorers in the Upper Peninsula panned the many creeks and rivers and occasionally found some "colors," but no bedrock deposits were ever located in this way. The geography of the U.P. differs from that of California in that the earth's surface in northern Michigan has been scoured and reshaped by the repeated advance and retreat of continental glaciers during the Pleistocene Epoch. The sand and gravel (and gold) in a stream bed here could have been eroded from bedrock nearby, or it could just as easily have come from hundreds of miles away, carried by an advancing glacier. Thus, gold in a river placer was no proof that a mother lode lay upstream. Nonetheless, gold placers are known to exist in Michigan, and mining them has often been proposed.

In the *Report of the State Board of Geological Survey of Michigan for the Year 1906,* William M. Courtis of Detroit, a mining engineer formerly associated with the Peninsular Gold Mining Company, listed the following placer gold finds:

Allegan County: Allegan.

Antrim County.

Charlevoix County: Boyne River.

Emmet County: Little Traverse River.

Ionia County: Maple River, Grand River below Lyons.

Iron County: Iron River.

Kalkaska County: Kalkaska, Rapid River, Walton.

Kent County: Lowell, Ada Creek.

Leelanau County: near Lake.

Marquette County: Ishpeming.

Manistee County: Little Sable River, Manistee River.

Montcalm County: Greenville, Howard City.

Newaygo County: County Line, Muskegon River.

Oakland County: Birmingham.

Oceana County: Elbridge, Hart, White River, Whitehall.

Ontonagon County: Flat River, Victoria Copper mine.

Ottawa County: Grand Haven.

St. Joseph County: Marcellus, Burr Oak.

Wexford County: Manistee River, West Summit.

Although a number of these finds were authenticated, others were believed to be just pyrite. It is doubtful that any of them is rich enough to be worked profitably.

The Carp River, which runs through the Ishpeming Gold Range as well as passing through large deposits of glacial drift, has been the source of a few placer gold reports. Around 1851, William A. Burt is reported to have found a nugget of gold in the Carp while building a dam. The nugget, which was the size of a bean, apparently was the only gold found. It didn't inspire any large-scale prospecting. Some years later, geologist Forest Sheppard was also reported to have found placer gold in the river.

In a report on the Dead River Gold Range written about 1890, Julius Ropes proposed placer mining in the many valleys in this rugged area. "That placer gold exists in quantities over all this area, to be profitably panned, cradled or sluiced, there is no doubt, tests made of sands and gravel in the ravines give every assurance," he wrote. However, Ropes was never known to do any placer mining in the region.

Some seven years before Captain Daniels opened the Original Sauk's Head Mine on Section 30, T50N-R26W, placer gold had been found in the same section. In a letter to the Marquette *Mining Journal,* homesteader George Rasmussen reported that he had taken samples of the sand from "a small stream of the finest running water you ever tasted" (apparently

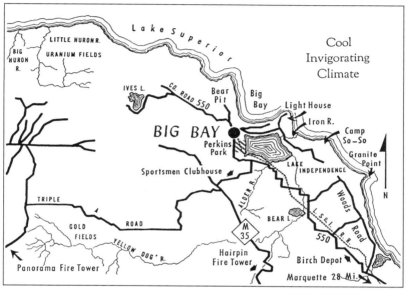

Sawmill Creek) as well as samples of rock from the area. When he brought them to Marquette for assay, the chemist reported both the sand and the rock samples showed a small quantity of gold. Rasmussen moved away from Michigan and never resumed his prospecting.

The Yellow Dog Plains, a deposit of glacial sand and gravel in northern Marquette County, have long been thought to contain placer gold. One of the earliest settlers on the plains, Nels Andersen, homesteaded on the SW ¼ of the SW ¼ of Section 35, T51N-R29W, from 1902 to 1913. While digging a well, he encountered a two-foot layer of black sand at a depth of 45 feet. Anderson felt that the black sand held

Tourist map showing "Gold Fields" on Yellow Dog Plains, circa 1950

Al Wood

gold. Some years later he had a sample assayed. His son claimed the assay showed $5.35 per ton in gold. While prospecting for the Michigan College of Mines in 1933, T.M. Broderick took a number of samples of sand and gravel from the Yellow Dog Plains and tested them for gold. A sample taken from Andersen's diggings proved to be the richest, showing 20 cents in gold per ton. Other samples from the plains assayed from three cents to 16 cents per ton.

An area of the Yellow Dog Plains southeast of Andersen's homestead was prospected in 1932 with dubious results. The McKay Company of Pittsburgh, Pennsylvania, set crews to work digging test pits and taking samples at numerous locations on the plains. A total of 107 samples were assayed, with values ranging from 12 cents to $2.69 per ton. The McKay Company's officials did not feel that the showing was worth developing and left the area before completing their negotiations with the owner of the land.

In 1934, the state geologist, apparently encouraged by Broderick's findings, proposed to search along the Yellow Dog River for placer gold. An agreement was reached whereby the landowners would furnish the necessary equipment, while men from the Civilian Conservation Corps camp at Big Bay would provide the manpower. The proposal was rejected by the Michigan Conservation Commission because it didn't fall within the scope of the Corps' work.

A few men worked the sands of the Yellow Dog River and other streams that cut through the glacial outwash plains during the Depression. Working on their own, these rugged individuals were sometimes able to make a living by panning and sluicing for gold. One man claimed to have averaged $5 per day while working a small stream in the northern part of the county.

The Yellow Dog Plains were sampled again in the 1970s by two mining companies and the United States Geological Survey. The results were disappointing to say the least — one of the companies reported finding only one "color" in 51 samples! The USGS reported finding no "colors" in 32 samples, and their assays showed less than .0006 ounces of gold per ton.

Gold was valued at $35 per ounce until 1971, and up to $195 by 1975.

In the late-1960s, retired electrical engineer Burnell Tindall and Don Malott, a Michigan State Highway Department expert on sand and gravel, along with two other partners, formed Au-Min-Co Incorporated. The company obtained contracts allowing them to work gravel pits in Clinton, Oakland and Washtenaw counties in the Lower Peninsula, sluicing the sand and gravel for heavy minerals and extracting gold from the concentrate by a secret process. Although at one point Tindall boasted that they had recovered $2 million in gold, actual recovery was much less. During one year, the company extracted $101 in gold, but incurred expenses of $20,000. When the other three partners moved away or died, Tindall kept up the work. Although yields increased, all work ceased with his death in 1976.

CHAPTER TEN

Fables
and Frauds

Many of the gold discoveries in Michigan's Upper Peninsula were too small or too poor to pay, but they generally held some amount of real gold. Along with these bona fide discoveries, however, the state also had its share of mythical mines, both fabulous and fraudulent.

Beginning in 1872, the Iron River area of Ontonagon County near present day Silver City was the site of a silver mining boom. A number of veins carrying native silver were discovered, and mining companies were formed to buy the land and work the veins. Several assays of the silver ore showed traces of gold, but the nature of the vein made the assayer and other geological experts doubt that gold would be found there. Eighteen months later, it was discovered that the specimens in question had indeed been salted with gold. Although the silver mines continued to produce in a small way for a number of years, no more talk was heard of gold mines in the area.

Like any mining area, Upper Michigan is home to many stories of "lost mines," tales of rich veins of gold and silver found by accident, never to be seen again. Larsen's gold is a typical example of these tales. In *Bloodstoppers and Bearwalkers,* a collection of folk tales from the U.P., author Richard Dorson quotes Jim Hodge of Negaunee:

"A fellow named Larsen was traveling north of Teal Lake, Negaunee, picking berries — lots of berries on the hills. He picked up a piece of quartz, attracted by the specks in it. If he'd been a mining man, he would have known there was gold in it. He put it in his pocket, and cut across the hills to town, to his brother's saloon. There was a mining man present; he said, 'Show it to me.' After he looked at it he said, 'I'd like to show that to a friend of mine.' He sent the piece to an assayer at Houghton, and it was assayed at $200 a ton in gold. But when Larsen went back to look for the quartz he couldn't find the spot, or even the hill.''

Perhaps the legend had a basis in fact, considering the gold find at the Korten prospect north of Teal Lake, but the value of the rock grew to legendary proportion!

Dorson also tells the tale of an elusive mine in the western Upper Peninsula, quoting Aaron Kinney of Iron River. ''Peter Paul's Gold Mine is on the south branch of the Paint, right below Uno Dam. Peter Paul came from Canada where they had gold, and here he found a piece of quartz that looked like gold. He was telling my father he'd strike the gold in a few strokes. He blast-drilled, sunk a shaft, single-jacking, twisting the drill himself. When he came down to water he had to quit, because he had only a hand pump. He was going to sell blueberries on the land around there to make a stake to develop his gold mine. People could pay him so much a quart to pick themselves. There were blueberries a solid mile up the river, you see. The dream of the gold mine never left him, but he never got a stake. He dug until he was too old to dig, and died without making a fortune. His place is still called Peter Paul's Gold Mine.''

Peter Paul's mine can still be seen today on the east bank of the Paint River, a few hundred yards off the Goldmine Truck Trail (USFS 151) between Beechwood and Gibbs City. Located on the SW ¼ of the NW ¼ of Section 13, T44N-R36W, the mine site includes the remains of the shaft and rock dump, as well as the ruins of Paul's homestead.

Around 1885, a man named Jack Grove crossed illegally from Canada into the Upper Peninsula and took up residence in the wilderness north of Champion. Grove had been a prospector in Canada. When he returned from one prospecting trip minus his partner, he was sought for questioning by the Royal Canadian Mounted Police. Rather than face the police, he decided to go to the U.S., where he lived alone the rest of his life.

While living his solitary life in a series of shacks near the headwaters of the Huron, Peshekee and Yellow Dog rivers, Jack Grove continued his prospecting and claimed to have found veins of gold-bearing quartz in several places near his camps. He wrote to the landowner, William C. Weber of Detroit, asking him for a one half interest in any gold he might discover. Weber refused to deal with Grove, but sent his own men into the woods to prospect his lands. Weber's men never found any gold, and Grove died without ever opening a mine.

Although traces of gold can be found in glacial gravels throughout Michigan, no economic deposits have ever been found in the Lower Peninsula. Nonetheless, the downstate area was host to a number of cases of gold fever. Probably the earliest example occurred in January 1848 when it was reported in *Hunt's Merchant's Magazine* that a gold strike had been made near downstate Tecumseh. Nuggets weighing up to an ounce and a half were rumored, and a company was to be formed to work the deposit. Apparently little work was done before the strike was found to be worthless.

The Alpena area was the site of one of the most successful "pocket mines" in Michigan (so named, not for the geological nature of the deposits, but because the only gold mined was from the pockets of investors). In 1924, a mining company was formed to work a reported vein of gold in the limestone of the region. Although there was no gold visible in the rock and independent assays failed to find any gold, the promoters assured potential investors that the "ore" held extremely finely divided gold that was too fine to be detected by normal assaying methods. The company's chemist laid claim to a wonderful method of recovering the fine gold. Investors from Michigan and Chicago were persuaded to put money into the venture,

and the company sank a shaft and diamond drilled in search of more veins. The shaft was put down 230 feet at a cost of $200,000, and a mill to put the chemist's method to work was built at a similar cost.

Within about a year, the Alpena gold boom died out. Investigations by the State Geological Survey revealed that ore samples had been salted. In one case, a specimen had been drilled out and gold inserted into the hole. In another, a sample had been treated with a chemical solution which deposited gold in the rock. With these revelations and with the investors' capital spent, the company's officials left town, leaving the empty shaft and silent mill as monuments to the gold seekers' eternal optimism.

With the 70 percent increase in the price of gold in 1934, gold fever again took hold in the Lower Peninsula, and even in Alpena again! Once more, a mining engineer discovered "micronic" gold, undetectable by ordinary means, and again a chemist came up with a means of extracting this elusive gold. This time, the charlatans were quickly unmasked and were forced to find other sheep to fleece.

A gold "rush" at Vernon in Shiawassee County was typical of the gold excitement of that era. An article in the *New York Times* told the story of a Native American who had made his living panning gold from the Shiawassee River many years before. In 1935, a grandson of the old Chippewa showed up with a birch-bark map pinpointing the location of the gold find. The grandson and his associates followed the map and started digging. The paper reported that the deposits turned up showed assay values equal to the best Klondike finds. Guards were stationed at the diggings, and the ore was sent to a smelter in Detroit. Similar gold booms occurred throughout the Lower Peninsula in the mid-1930s, notably in Montrose, Ortonville, Perry and Grand Rapids. It seems that none of these "pocket mines" ever panned out, but made money only for their promoters.

Even the Ropes Gold Mine, where gold mining had been proven to be economically feasible, was the source of at least one picturesque lie. In its October 31, 1894 issue, the Chicago *Inter Ocean* ran this "Special Telegram:"

"A report comes from the Ropes Gold Mine, near here, that at the bottom level a spring has been struck which supplies a strong stream of highly colored water, being nearly as yellow as gold and plainly holding considerable of that precious material in its solution. It is very palatable and ice cold. Several of the men working in that level have been in the habit of freely drinking the water and it was noticed that as they drank the desire for alcoholic stimulants died within them. Some of the men have been heavy drinkers of beer and whiskey but since the use of this water they had no use for any stimulants. Their health and physical condition is generally improved and it is thought that the water is a veritable and natural 'gold cure,' not only for the liquor habit but for general diseases of all kinds. There is some talk of erecting a huge hospital at the mine, using the water as a cure-all for the ills of men."

The story was quickly picked up and debunked by the local papers (such a solution of gold in water being chemically impossible) but not before the mine management received a number of inquiries about the cure.

Epilogue

Despite the failure of the early prospects in Michigan, the Ishpeming Gold Range continues to attract prospectors. Exploration and mining companies have prospected the old workings and searched for new veins, with the same varying results as the old timers. Among the companies which have participated in this continuing search for precious metals has been the Cleveland Cliffs Iron Company, working both independently and in joint ventures with others. In 1966, Cleveland Cliffs diamond drilled at the Michigan Gold Mine, looking for continuations of the gold veins. Cleveland Cliffs and Bethlehem Steel formed the Beth-Cliffs Joint Venture and explored for precious metals in the 1970s. In 1977, Cliffs joined with Chevron Oil as the NOMEX AU Joint Venture and diamond drilled at Bjork and Lundin's exploration and other locations west of the Ropes Gold Mine.

Between 1968 and 1971, the Humble Oil Company (later to become Exxon) explored for massive sulfides and precious metals north of the Dead River, and diamond drilled near Clark Creek and in the Reany Lake area. A joint venture involving the Superior Oil Company and Nicor Mineral Ventures also prospected in the Dead River area from 1972 to 1985. This joint venture drilled 14 diamond drill holes in the vicinity of the Holyoke Silver Mine. Other companies which are known to have prospected on the gold range include Kerr McGee, Phelps Dodge and St. Joe American Corporation.

A systematic geological mapping of the greenstone belt north of the Dead River has been under way since 1984. A cooperative venture between the Geological Survey Division of the Michigan Department of Natural Resources and the Department of Geology and Geological Engineering of Michigan Technological University, the project has involved MTU students and faculty as well as DNR geologists. The geology of more than 40 square miles of the greenstone belt has been mapped and sampled, and several areas of anomalous gold and silver concentration have been identified.

Since the closing of the Ropes Mine, Callahan Mining Corporation has continued its exploration program, hoping to find further reserves of gold-bearing rock. The company holds title to the Michigan, Superior and Peninsular gold mining properties west of the Ropes, where diamond drilling has been done to evaluate the ore bodies. Sufficiently rich ore was found at the old Peninsular Gold Mine that at one time Callahan considered reopening the mine. The company has also done diamond drilling and intensive sampling at Bjork and Lundin's exploration west of the Ropes and in the Silver Creek area north of the Dead River. Early in 1991, Callahan entered into a joint venture with Western Mining Corporation (USA) and Cleveland Cliffs Iron Company to explore for gold in the vicinity of the closed Champion Iron Ore Mine, some 13 miles west of the Ropes.

In most of these 20th century explorations, it seems that the prospectors have met with the same results as their 19th century counterparts — small areas of promising ore grade, but not enough ore to open a paying mine. Still, favorable geological conditions and continuing discoveries of gold ore keep the prospectors at work. If they ever find an ore body as rich as the 19th century miners' hopes, perhaps the Ishpeming Gold Range will once again be mined.

Glossary

ADIT	A horizontal or nearly horizontal entrance to a mine.
AMALGAM	An alloy of mercury with gold and/or silver.
ASSAY	Analysis of an ore to determine its composition and value.
BACKREAM	To enlarge a drill hole by pulling a reamer through the hole.
BULLION	Gold or silver considered in mass rather than in value.
CHALCOCITE	Cuprous sulfide, an important ore of copper.
CHALCOPYRITE	A yellow sulfide of copper and iron.
CHIMNEY	A vertical rich streak in a vein.
CONCENTRATE	A product containing the valuable metal from which most of the waste material in the ore has been eliminated.
CROSSCUT	A horizontal underground opening driven across the strike of the vein.
DIAMOND DRILL	A drill having a hollow, cylindrical bit set with diamonds, used for obtaining cores of rock samples.
DIORITE	A granular igneous rock consisting essentially of plagioclase feldspar and hornblende.
DIP	The vertical angle formed by a vein and the surface.
DORÉ	Unrefined gold bullion containing other metals.
DRIFT	A horizontal passage running through or parallel to a vein.
FLOAT COPPER	Loose fragments of copper that have been moved from one place to another by the action of glaciers.
FORTY	A 40-acre parcel of land, generally a quarter mile square.
FREE GOLD	Gold which can be extracted from the ore by amalgamation with mercury.
GALENA	A sulfide of lead, the most common lead ore.
GRIZZLY	A grating placed over the top of a chute for the purpose of stopping the larger pieces of ore.
HEADFRAME	The framework over a mine shaft which supports the hoisting apparatus.
LEVEL	The horizontal passages at a given depth in a mine.
LODE	A body of mineral deposited between clearly defined rock walls; a vein.

MANGANESE	Hard, brittle, grayish-white metallic element used chiefly as an alloying agent in steel to give it toughness.
MILL	A plant in which ore is treated to recover the valuable metals. Also a machine to grind the ore.
OPTION	The exclusive right to explore a parcel of land for minerals, or to purchase the land for a specified price.
PLACER	A deposit of sand or gravel containing minerals eroded out of their original occurrence.
PROSPECT	*n.* 1. A site believed to host a mineral deposit, or the workings at such a site. *v.* 2. To search for mineral deposits.
PYRITE	A sulfide of iron, commonly called "fool's gold."
QUARTZ	A hard, glassy mineral, silicon dioxide, in which gold is often found.
RIFFLE	A lining at the bottom of a sluice arranged in such a manner that grooves or openings are left for catching and collecting particles of gold.
SALT	To introduce rich ore or other valuable matter fraudulently into a mine or a mineral sample to create a false impression of value.
SECTION	A mile-square parcel of land.
SHAFT	A vertical or steeply angled entrance to a mine.
SILVER-LEAD	Galena (a lead ore) containing silver.
SKIP	A self-dumping bucket used to hoist ore up a shaft.
SLUICE	*n.* 1. A long, sloping trough or the like, with grooves in its bottom, into which water is directed to separate gold from gravel or sand. *v.* 2. To wash in a sluice.
SMELTER	A furnace for extracting metal from ore by the application of heat.
STAMP MILL	A mill or machine in which ore is crushed to powder by means of heavy stamps or pestles.
STOPE	An opening from which ore is removed.
STRIKE	The direction of the surface exposure of a vein.
SUGAR QUARTZ	A white, granular form of quartz.
SULFIDE MINERALS	A compound of sulfur and a metal, often valued as an ore of the metal.
TAILINGS	The ground rock left after the gold has been extracted.
TAILRACE	The channel for conducting tailings away in water.

TALCOSE	Containing the soft, soapy mineral talc.
TELLURIUM	A silvery-white metal which sometimes occurs in combination with gold.
TRAM	A small-wheeled car running on rails used to transport ore.
TRESTLE	A frame typically composed of a horizontal bar or beam rigidly joined or fitted at each end to the top of a transverse A-frame, used to support a railroad or tramway.
TROY	A system of weights used to weigh precious metals. A troy ounce is equal to 1.097 common avoirdupois ounces.
VANNER	An inclined vibrating rubber belt used to concentrate heavy mineral ores.
VEIN	A long, narrow body of mineral; a lode.

INDEX

151

152

Bibliography

Allen, R.C. "Gold in Michigan," *Mineral Resources of Michigan with Statistical Tables of Production and Value of Mineral Products for 1910 and Prior Years*. Michigan Geological and Biological Survey, Publication 8, Series 6, pp. 355-366. Lansing, Michigan. State Printers. 1912.

Barnett, LeRoy. *Mining in Michigan: A Catalog of Company Publications 1845-1980*. Marquette, Michigan. Northern Michigan University Press. 1983.

Barton Jr., P.B. and F.O. Simon. "Gold Content of Michigan Native Copper," *Geological Survey Research 1972, Chapter A*, p. A-4. Professional Paper 800-A. United States Geological Survey.

Baxter, D.A., T.J. Bornhorst and J.L. VanAlstine. *Geology, Structure and Associated Precious Metal Mineralization of Archean Rocks in the Vicinity of Clark Creek, Marquette County, Michigan*. Open File Report OFR 87-8, Geological Survey Division. Michigan Department of Natural Resources. 1987.

Beard's Directory and History of Marquette County. Detroit, Michigan. Hadger & Bryce, Steam Book Printers. 1873.

Benedict, C. Harry. *Lake Superior Milling Practice*. Houghton, Michigan. The Michigan College of Mining and Technology. 1955.

Biographical Record. Chicago, Illinois. Biographical Publishing Company. 1903.

Boben, C.L., T.J. Bornhorst and J.L. VanAlstine. *Detailed Geological Study of Three Precious Metal Prospects in Marquette County and One in Gogebic County, Michigan*. Open File Report OFR 86-1, Geological Survey Division. Michigan Department of Natural Resources. 1986.

Bodwell, Willard Arthur. *Geological Compilation and Nonferrous Metal Potential of the Precambrian Section of Northern Michigan*. MS Thesis. Michigan Technological University. 1972.

Bornhorst, Theodore J., Anthony W. Shepeck and Dean M. Rossell. "The Ropes Gold Mine, Marquette County, Michigan, U.S.A. — An Archean Hosted Lode Gold Deposit," in MacDonald, A.J., ed., *Proceedings of Gold '86, an International Symposium on the Geology of Gold*, pp. 213-227. Toronto, Ontario. 1986.

Bradish, Alvah. *Memoir of Douglass Houghton*. Detroit, Michigan. Raynor & Taylor, Printers. 1889.

Broderick, T.M. "Geology of the Ropes Gold Mine," *Bulletin of the Michigan College of Mining and Technology*. Houghton, Michigan. June 1945.

Brozdowski, Robert A., Richard J. Gleason and Glenn W. Scott. "The Ropes Mine: A Pyritic Gold Deposit in Volcaniclastic Rock, Ishpeming, Michigan, U.S.A.," in MacDonald, A.J., ed., *Proceedings of Gold '86, an International Symposium on the Geology of Gold,* pp. 228-242. Toronto, Ontario. 1986.

Callahan Mining Corporation. *Annual Report.* 1980-1987.

Cannon, William F. and John S. Klasner. *Bedrock Geologic Map of the Southern Part of the Diorite and Champion 7½ Minute Quadrangles, Marquette County, Michigan.* U.S. Geological Survey Miscellaneous Investigations Series Map I-1058. 1977.

The Chicago Times, March 5, 1864. Chicago, Illinois.

Clark, L.D., William F. Cannon and John S. Klasner. *Bedrock Geologic Map of the Negaunee SW Quadrangle, Marquette County, Michigan.* U.S. Geological Survey Geologic Quadrangle Map GQ-1226. 1975.

Clarke, Don H. *The Gold Mines of Michigan.* 1976.

Courtis, W.M. "Gold in Michigan," *Michigan Geological Service Annual Report,* pp. 581-584. 1906.

Denning, R.M. "Geology of the Ishpeming Gold Range." Michigan Geological Survey Open File Report. 1948.

Detroit Free Press, June 14, July 3, 1889. Detroit, Michigan.

Detroit News, August 18, 1935. Detroit, Michigan.

Dorr, J.A. and D.F. Eschman. *Geology of Michigan.* Ann Arbor, Michigan. The University Press. 1970.

Edwards, James P. *Mines and Mineral Statistics,* pp. 113-115. Lansing, Michigan. Robert Smith and Company. 1892.

The Engineering and Mining Journal, various issues. The Scientific Publishing Company.

Evening News, August 28, 1888. Detroit, Michigan.

Fuller, George N., ed. *Geological Reports of Douglass Houghton.* Lansing, Michigan. The Michigan Historical Commission. 1928.

Gair, Jacob E. and Robert E. Thaden. *Geology of the Marquette and Sands Quadrangles, Marquette, Michigan.* U.S. Geological Survey Professional Paper 397. 1968.

"The Gold Fields," *The Engineering and Mining Journal,* August 18, 1888.

Gold in Michigan. Open File Report MGSD OFR GOLD 80-1, Geological Survey Division. Michigan Department of Natural Resources. 1980.

"Gold Mines of Michigan," *The New York Times,* August 27, 1888.

Hawke, Richard. *A Guide to Rocks and Minerals of Michigan.* Midland, Michigan. Dick Hawke Science Service. 1981.

Heinrich, E. William. *The Mineralogy of Michigan.* Geological Bulletin 6. Lansing, Michigan. State Printers. 1976.

History of the Upper Peninsula of Michigan. Chicago, Illinois. The Western Historical Company. 1883.

Holland, A.H. *1891 Handbook and Guide to Ishpeming, Michigan, Together with a Mining Directory of Marquette County.*

Holland, A.H. *A Gazetteer of Marquette County.* Marquette, Michigan. Mining Journal Print. 1889.

Holland, A.H. *The Marquette City Directory.* Marquette, Michigan. Mining Journal Print. 1891.

Holland, A.H. and E.H. Dwight. *1886-7 Handbook and Guide to Ishpeming, L.S., Michigan.* Marquette, Michigan. Mining Journal Book and Job Print. 1886.

Holland, A.H. and E.H. Dwight. *1886-7 Handbook and Guide to Marquette, L.S., Michigan.* Marquette, Michigan. Mining Journal Book and Job Print. 1886.

The Iron Agitator, various issues, 1881 through 1886. Ishpeming, Michigan.

The Iron Herald, various issues, 1884 through 1894. Negaunee, Michigan.

The Iron Home, various issues, 1874. Ishpeming, Michigan.

The Iron Ore, various issues, 1886 through 1953. Ishpeming, Michigan.

"The Ishpeming Gold Range," *The Engineering and Mining Journal,* July 5, 1890.

Johnson, R.C., T.J. Bornhorst and J.L. VanAlstine. *Geology and Precious Metal Mineralization of the Silver Creek to Rocking Chair Lakes Area, Marquette County, Michigan.* Open File Report OFR 86-2, Geological Survey Division. Michigan Department of Natural Resources. 1986.

Jopling, James E. "Personal Reminiscences of a Mining Engineer," *Michigan History Magazine,* April 1927.

Kelly, W.A. *Economic Geology of the Dead River Area.* Unpublished manuscript (report to the Norgan Gold Mining Company). 1936.

Kelly, W.A. *Geology of the Dead River Area, Marquette County, Michigan.* Unpublished manuscript (report to the Norgan Gold Mining Company). 1936.

Knight, James B. *Mines and Mineral Statistics,* pp. 159-160. Lansing, Michigan. Robert Smith and Company. 1894.

Koschman, A.H. and M.H. Bergendahl. *Principal Gold Producing Districts of the U.S.* Geological Survey Professional Paper 610. Washington, D.C. Government Printing Office. 1962.

Kronquist, E.A. *Report on Exploration of Section 35, T49N-R27W, Michigan.* Unpublished manuscript (report to the Norgan Gold Mining Company). 1936.

LaFayette, Kenneth. *Marquette Gold and Silver Finds.* Unpublished manuscript. Marquette Historical Society. 1975.

Lake Superior Journal, August 7, 21, 1850; April 1, September 15, 1852; April 5, 1857; January 2, 1964. Sault Ste. Marie, Michigan.

Lake Superior News and Mining Journal, August 8, 22, 1846. Copper Harbor, Michigan.

Lamey, Carl A. *Michigan Gold.* Unpublished manuscript, Geology Department. Michigan College of Mining and Technology. 1935.

Lamey, Carl A. *Notes Regarding Geological Conditions Observed During Summer of 1936, Norgan Gold Mining Company, Section 35, T47N-R27W.* Unpublished manuscript (report to the Norgan Gold Mining Company). 1936.

Lane, Alfred C. *Report of the State Board of Geological Survey of Michigan for the Year 1904,* pp. 156-158. Lansing, Michigan. 1905.

Lane, Alfred C. *Report of the State Board of Geological Survey of Michigan for the Year 1906,* pp. 581-584. Lansing, Michigan. 1907.

"Large Nuggets of Gold," *The New York Times,* July 21, 1888, p. 1.

Lawton, Charles D. *Mineral Resources,* p. 157-161. Lansing, Michigan. Thorp and Godfrey. 1886.

Lawton, Charles D. *Mines and Mineral Statistics,* pp. 269-273. Lansing, Michigan. Thorp and Godfrey. 1887.

Lawton, Charles D. *Mines and Mineral Statistics,* pp. 137-143. Lansing, Michigan. Thorp and Godfrey. 1888.

Lawton, Charles D. *Mines and Mineral Statistics,* pp. 91-100. Lansing, Michigan. Darius D. Thorp. 1889.

Lawton, Charles D. *Mines and Mineral Statistics,* pp. 65-69. Lansing, Michigan. Robert Smith and Company. 1890.

Lawton, Charles D. *Mines and Mineral Statistics,* p. 83. Lansing, Michigan. Robert Smith and Company. 1891.

Margeson, G.B., J.W. Norby, R.A. Brozdowski, A.S. Carter and B.A. Bouley. "Comparison of Two Parts of the Dead River-Ishpeming Greenstone Belt: Evidence for Correlation of Volcanic Stratigraphy," (abs.): *Institute on Lake Superior Geology Proceedings and Abstracts,* V. 34, Part I, p. 70. 1988.

"The Michigan Gold Fields," *The New York Times,* September 2, 1888, p. 9.

"The Michigan Gold Mines," *The New York Times,* July 30, 1888, p. 5.

Michigan State Gazetteer and Business Directory, Volume V. Detroit, Michigan. R.L. Polk & Co. 1881.

Michigan State Gazetteer and Business Directory, Volume VII. Detroit, Michigan. R.L. Polk & Co. 1885.

Michigan State Gazetteer and Business Directory, Volume VIII. Detroit, Michigan. R.L. Polk & Co. 1887.

Michigan State Gazetteer and Business Directory, Volume X. Detroit, Michigan. R.L. Polk & Co. 1891.

Mineral Processing Flowsheets. Denver, Colorado. Denver Equipment Company. 1962.

Mining Journal, various issues, 1881-1990. Marquette, Michigan.

Nankervis, James L. *Mines and Mineral Statistics,* p. 218. Houghton, Michigan. Gazette Print. 1908.

Newett, George A. *Mines and Mineral Statistics,* pp. 164-170. Lansing, Michigan. Robert Smith and Company. 1896.

Newett, George A. *Mines and Mineral Statistics,* pp. 169-172. Ishpeming, Michigan. Iron Ore Printing House. 1897.

Newett, George A. *Mines and Mineral Statistics,* p. 200. Ishpeming, Michigan. Iron Ore Printing House. 1898.

Newett, George A. *Mines and Mineral Statistics,* p. 289. Ishpeming, Michigan. Iron Ore Printing House. 1899.

Newett, George A. "A Michigan Gold Mine," *Michigan History Magazine,* Vol. 11, No. 1, pp. 73-91. 1927.

The New York Times, July 16, 1887; July 26, August 28, September 7, 10, 1888.

Norby, J.W. "History of Precious Metal Exploration/Development in the Dead River-Ishpeming Greenstone Belt," (abs.): *Institute on Lake Superior Geology Proceedings and Abstracts,* V. 34, Part I, p. 82-84. 1988.

Owens, E.O. and T.J. Bornhorst. *Geology and Precious Metal Mineralization of the Fire Center and Holyoke Mines Area, Marquette County, Michigan.* Open File Report OFR 85-2, Geological Survey Division. Michigan Department of Natural Resources. 1985.

Pardee, Franklin G. "Michigan's Mythical Gold Mines," *Michigan Conservation,* Vol. 14, No. 11, November 1945, pp. 5, 9-10.

Parker, Richard A. "The New Michigan Gold Finds," *The Engineering and Mining Journal,* September 22, 1888, pp. 238-239.

Portage Lake Mining Gazette, April 9, 1864. Houghton, Michigan.

Puffett, Willard P. *Geology of the Negaunee Quadrangle, Marquette County, Michigan.* U.S. Geological Survey Professional Paper 788. 1974.

Puffett, Willard P. *Occurrences of Base Metals South of Dead River, Negaunee Quadrangle, Marquette County, Michigan,* p. 18. 12th Annual Institute of Lake Superior Geology. 1966.

Quirke, T.T. *Preliminary Geological Report, T49N-R27W Section 35, Marquette County, Michigan.* Unpublished manuscript (report to the Norgan Gold Mining Company). 1936.

Rainbow Exploration Company. *Geology of the Eagle Mills-Morgan Area.* Unpublished geological map. circa 1988.

"Rich Gold Deposits Found in Michigan," *The New York Times,* December 8, 1935.

Robers, W. Chandler. "Gold," *Encyclopedia Britannica.* Chicago, Illinois. The Werner Company. 1894.

Robinson, Orrin W. *Early Days of the Lake Superior Copper Country.* Houghton, Michigan. D.L. Robinson. 1938.

Russell, James. *Mines and Mineral Statistics,* p. 127. Marquette, Michigan. Mining Journal Company Ltd. 1901.

Rydholm, C. Fred. *Superior Heartland: A Backwoods History.* Marquette, Michigan. Privately published by the author. 1989.

Schmeling, E.S. *Report on T49N-R28W, Sections 1, 2, 3, 10-15, T49N-R27W, Sections 6, 7 & 18.* Unpublished manuscript (report to the Norgan Gold Mining Company). 1936.

Seagall, R. Tom and Glenna Seagall. "14 Years of 24 Karat Mining," *Michigan Natural Resources,* Vol. 44, No. 6, November-December 1975, pp. 7-9.

Seeland, David A. *A Geochemical Reconnaissance for Gold in the Sedimentary Rocks of the Great Lakes Region, Minnesota to New York.* U.S. Geological Survey Bulletin 1305. 1973.

Skillings, David N. "Callahan Begins Development of its Ropes Gold Mine for 1985 Operation," *Skillings Mining Review,* September 17, 1983.

Snelgrove, A.K., W.A. Seaman and V.L. Ayres. *Strategic Minerals Investigations in Marquette and Baraga Counties.* 1943 Michigan Geological Survey Progress Report No. 10. 1944.

Snider, David W. *Investigation of a Reported Copper-Silver Showing in Section 30, T50N, R26W, Marquette County, Michigan.* Open File Report OFR 77-2, Geological Survey Division. Michigan Department of Natural Resources. 1977.

Sprague, Marshall. *Money Mountain; The Story of Cripple Creek Gold.* Boston, Massachusetts. Little, Brown and Company. 1953.

Stonehouse, Frederick. *Marquette Shipwrecks.* Au Train, Michigan. Avery Color Studios. 1977.

Swineford, Alfred P. *Annual Report of the Commissioner of Mineral Statistics of the State of Michigan for 1883,* pp. 98-100, 112-117. Marquette, Michigan. Marquette Mining Journal Publishing House. 1884.

Swineford, Alfred P. *Annual Report of the Commissioner of Mineral Statistics of the State of Michigan for 1884,* pp. 9-11. Marquette, Michigan. Marquette Mining Journal Publishing House. 1885.

Swineford, Alfred P. *History and Review of the Copper, Iron, Silver, Slate and Other Material Interests of the South Shore of Lake Superior,* p. 65-67. Marquette, Michigan. *The Mining Journal.* 1876.

Thirtell, Joel. "Gold Fever," *Detroit Free Press,* May 15, 1991. Detroit, Michigan.

Tyler, Stan. *Sections 8, 9, Northern Half of 16 & 17, etc., T49N-R27W.* Unpublished manuscript (report to the Norgan Gold Mining Company). 1936.

Wadsworth, M.E. "A Sketch of the Geology of the Iron, Gold and Copper Districts," *Report of the State Board of Geological Survey for the Years 1891 and 1892,* pp. 152-155. Michigan Geological Survey. Lansing, Michigan. 1893.

Wakefield Bulletin, various issues, 1887-1888. Wakefield, Michigan.

Wayment, Ross, Ropes Unit Manager, Callahan Mining Corporation. Interview February 7, 1985.

Zinn, Justin. *Field Report Covering the Field Mapping in 1936 for the Norgan Gold Mining Company.* Unpublished manuscript (report to the Norgan Gold Mining Company). 1936.

About the Author

Daniel R. Fountain is a historian who embraces an avid interest in the rich and colorful history of early Michigan settlers and miners. Raised in the Upper Peninsula of Michigan, he grew up in an area where mining was, and continues to be, the livelihood of most residents. Dan holds an Associate Degree in Electronics from Northern Michigan University.

For the past 10 years, Dan has conducted extensive research on gold mining in Michigan. He has spend countless hours in museums and libraries seeking detailed historical documentation, and has hiked many miles in the rugged forests of Upper Michigan in search of the numerous gold mining prospects about which he writes.

Dan has served on the board of directors and as president of the Negaunee Historical Society, continuing to be involved in on-going research concerning gold mining and other subjects of local historical significance. In addition to prospecting, in his leisure time Dan enjoys traveling, photography, scuba diving and shipwreck research. Dan and his wife, Judy, live in Negaunee, Michigan.

LS
PC

Other publications of Lake Superior Port Cities Inc.

Julius F. Wolff Jr.'s Lake Superior Shipwrecks
  Hardcover: ISBN 0-942235-02-9
  Softcover: ISBN 0-942235-01-0

Shipwrecks of Lake Superior by James R. Marshall
  Softcover: ISBN 0-942235-00-2

Shipwreck of the Mesquite by Frederick Stonehouse
  Softcover: ISBN 0-942235-10-x

The Superior Way, Second Edition by Bonnie Dahl
  Softcover: ISBN 0-942235-14-2

Lake Superior Magazine (Bimonthly)

Lake Superior Newsletter (Quarterly)

Lake Superior Travel Guide (Annual)

Lake Superior Wall Calendar (Annual)

Great Lakes Wall Calendar (Annual)

For a catalog of the entire Lake Superior Port Cities collection of
books and merchandise, write or call:

Lake Superior Port Cities Inc.
P.O. Box 16417
Duluth, Minnesota 55816-0417
USA

218-722-5002
800-635-0544
FAX 218-722-4096

Dear Consumer:

You're holding one of the fine products of our publishing company, Lake Superior Port Cities Inc. We've been producing magazines, calendars, books and the like since 1979. If you're not already receiving our mailings, we'd be happy to share information with you about our other products through our periodic catalogs. Our flagship bimonthly is *Lake Superior Magazine* which is accompanied by the annual *Lake Superior Travel Guide*. From calendars of the Great Lakes and Lake Superior to tales about the history, shipwrecks and sailing on the big lake, our team invites you to get in touch with the more interesting aspects of life on the largest fresh-water lake in the world.

Lake Superior Port Cities Inc.
325 Lake Avenue South
Duluth, Minnesota 55802   USA
218-722-5002

Call for our free catalog of fine products

800-635-0544

We hope you enjoy this publication from Lake Superior Port Cities Inc.

Book Title _____

How you learned about this book _____

Purchased at_____

Comments _____

_____

☐ Please send me *Lake Superior Magazine*'s FREE catalog of regional gifts and add my name to the mailing list for information on future publications. Lake Superior Port Cities Inc. does not sell its mailing list to other organizations.

Name_____

Address _____

City _____

State/Province _____   ZIP + 4/Postal Code _____

_____

☐ Please send a FREE catalog to the name listed below. It is not necessary to include the names of those who have ordered from us in the past.

Name_____

Address _____

City _____

State/Province _____   ZIP + 4/Postal Code _____